The BERKSHIRE Weather Book

Berkshire is in the heart of Southern England and no part of it is far from the River Thames, or the many tributaries which feed it. The mood of the Thames is greatly influenced by the weather and in recent years the sheer intensity of rain has frequently turned it into a roaring torrent. Millions of gallons of water have invaded farmsteads, hamlets, villages and towns. There have been glorious balmy days when people have sunbathed on its banks, and there have been those frosty occasions when it has been possible to walk on the ice across the river. If the Thames dominates life in this landlocked but much-loved county, the weather certainly supplies the variety. Raging blizzards, surprise tornadoes, devastating landslides and even mudslides, violent thunderstorms, hurricane-force winds and the longest drought in history are just part of the recent history of Berkshire. There has been more — much more-- and in this unique pictorial record we have the evidence.

Ian Currie, Mark Davison and Bob Ogley

Froglets Publications

and Frosted Earth

Froglets Publications Ltd, Brasted Chart, Westerham, Kent TN16 1LY
Tel: 0959 562972   Fax: 0959 565365

© 1994

Ian Currie, Mark Davison and Bob Ogley

ISBN: 1 872337 48 1

Cover illustrations

Front cover: Skating on Abingdon Lock in Old Berkshire in 1895. Courtesy of the Oxfordshire Photographic Archive, Centre for Oxfordshire Studies

Back cover: Milkman John Kirby of Bracknell delivers to houses in flooded Maidenhead in 1990. For 10 days he continued to deliver to more than 200 marooned customers. Courtesy Reading Evening Post.

This book was originated by Froglets Publications Ltd of Brasted Chart and printed and bound by Staples Printers Rochester Ltd

Map and cover design by Alison Stammers

Additonal research, editing and design by Fern Flynn

Acknowledgements

MANY people gave us great advice and practical help in the preparation of this book. Thanks go to the editors of evening and weekly newspapers who published our appeal for help and to those who replied, confirming that Berkshire is well renowned for its great variety of weather. We are grateful for the assistance given by newspaper photographic staff, curators of museums, library staff, the National Rivers Authority and archivists throughout Berkshire.

Special thanks also to Radio Berkshire, Mercury Sound, Reading Evening Post, Reading Newspaper Company,, Maidenhead Advertiser, Newbury Weekly News, Slough Observer, Windsor, Slough and Eton Express, Bracknell News, the Royal Meteorological Society, the Meteorological Office (Bracknell), Mrs C. Clarke, British Rainfall, Climatological Observers Link. Journal of Meteorology, Roger Brugge, Bernard Burton. We are particularly indebted to Nuala la Vertue and Margaret Smith, to Brian Girling for allowing us to reproduce his historic postcards and to all other photographic sources as listed below.

We refer to certain publications including *A Century of London Weather* (J.H.Brazell), *The Weather of Britain* (Robin Stirling), *Parson in Vale of White Horse* (George Woodward), *British Floods and Droughts* (Brooks and Glasspoole), *Storm Force* (Reading Evening Post), *Hurricane Force* (George Hill).

Photographic credits

Oxfordshire Photographic Archive, Centre for Oxfordshire Studies: 5 (top), 9, 15, 16/17, 18, 19, 20/21, 28, 29, 30, 31, 32, 37, 55, 57. **Reading Evening Post**: 24, 43, 52, 61, 66, 85, 89 (t), 91, 92, 94 (t), 95 (t), 98 (bottom), 100 (b), 102 (t), 103, 104, 105, 107, 109, 111, 118 (b), 119, 120 (b), 121, 124, 126 (t), 127 (b), 130, 131, 133. **Royal County of Berkshire Cultural Services, Library and Information Services**: 27, 35, 36 (t), 49, 50, 53, 54 (t), 64/65, 71 (b), 72 (t), 73, 74, 93, 99 (t). **Topham Picture Library:** 60, 69, 70, 71 (t), 72 (b), 75, 76, 78, 80, 81,83, 120 (t), 126 (b), 128. **Peter Bloodworth (for Newbury Weekly News):** 115 (t), 125, 134 (b), 137 (b). **Newbury Weekly News**: 38, 40 (b), 62, 63. **Frank W. Cooper (for Newbury Weekly News):** 101.**Rural History Centre, University of Reading**: 23, 34, 36 (b), 56, 58, 59, 84. **David and Marion Canning**: 86, 88, 90, 94 (b), 95 (b), 99, 102 (b), 106, 108, 132. **Bill Pike**: 100 (t), 110, 112, 134 (t), 135 (t). **J.F.P. Galvin:** 114, 115 (b). **Reading Museum Service (Reading Chronicle Collection)**: 68, 82. **Slough and Windsor Express Newspaper Group:** 98 (t), 138. **Bracknell News:** 117, 118 (t). **Harrison:** 7, 25 (b). **Illustrated London News:** 11. **Newbury District Museum:** 12, 46. **Royal County of Berkshire Record Office:** 14. **National Railway Museum**: 26. **Rosemary Oldfield**: 44. **Dr. H.D. Astley Hope:** 45, 54 (b). **British Waterways:** 97. **Sue Hopson Postcards (RHCUR):** 47. **Ian Currie:** 5 (b), 39, 48. **Fern Flynn:** 127 (t). **Ian Smith (The Faringdon Folly):** 135 (b), 137 (t). **J.Holloway:** 77. **J.Jones:** 79. **E.D. Hutchins:** 89 (b).**Maidenhead Advertiser:**101, 139. **HMSO:** 141. **Brian Girling:** 24, 40 (t), 41, 42.

THE ROYAL COUNTY OF BERKSHIRE, INCLUDING THE TRADITIONAL BOUNDARIES

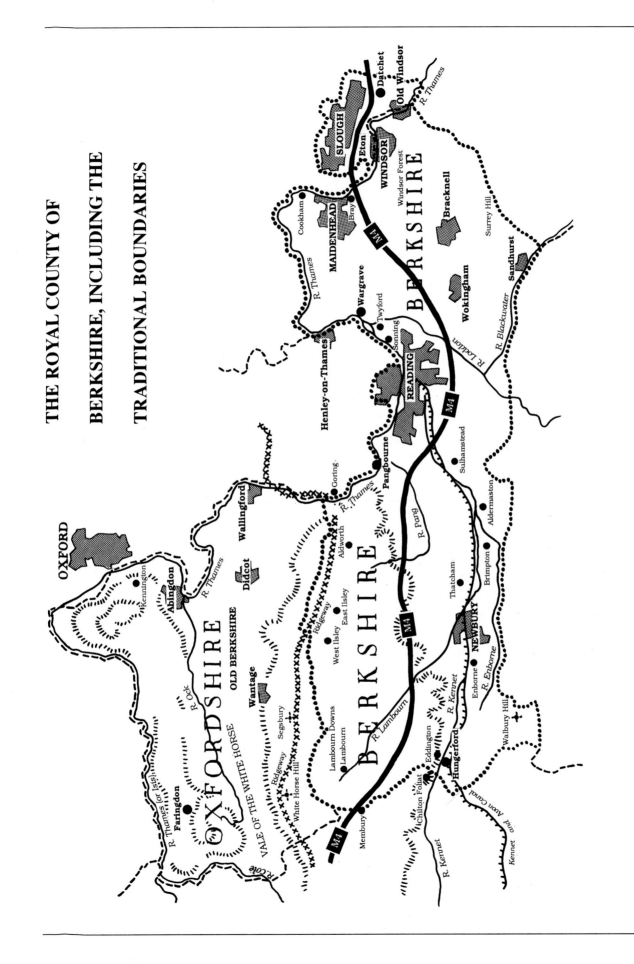

Fire, floods, frost and fog

BERKSHIRE, it has been said, is not a county to inspire immense works of literature. Apart from Windsor, there are few great tourist attractions, no cathedrals, no famous monuments, no great lakes. There are no eroding cliffs or vanishing villages, no great mountains to climb or rapids to conquer. But Berkshire has subtlety and a scenery as varied as any, from thatched villages of mellow stone to fertile farmland, from ancient forests to sweeping Downs, from lush meadows to fine gardens. It also has the most famous river in England, the Thames, whose mood is governed almost entirely by the weather.

From the time that man first learned the art of navigation he has experienced a long and remarkable association with the Thames and its moods. There have been whirlwinds and tornadoes, great storms and gales of hurricane force. Thunder has echoed along the valleys which have been majestically illuminated by flashes of lightning. Blizzards have swept across the plains to the water's edge, leaving behind great drifts. The river waters have been enraged and enlarged by melting snow or violent deluges, banks have burst and swirling, muddy floods have lapped ancient streets and river meadows. People who love the river have often wept at its cruelty.

Frequent boundary changes have disrupted Berkshire's history. In 1974, the administrators, for the sake of convenience, gave more than a third of the county to Oxfordshire. The boundary used to run along the River Cole to the Upper Thames (or Isis) all the way to Runnymede. Today it zigzags a course from the M4 near Lambourn to the A417 near Streatley and old Berkshire towns and villages, like Wantage, Wallingford, Abingdon and Didcot have been given to Oxfordshire. As the weather has no distinctions this book refers to the historical boundaries of Berkshire.

To the inhabitants, like those of other counties, the weather is a perpetual topic of conversation, especially in times of great floods and gales. It is not only the Thames which bursts its banks and floods farmland, village and town. The Kennet, Lambourn, Blackwater, Pang, Theale, Enborne, Ock, Cole and the Kennet and Avon Canal have all brought their share of drama and heartbreak. Many floods have been tagged as "the worst in living memory". Those in 1894 and 1947 have certainly earned a place in Berkshire folklore.

Away from the rivers the county has experienced other extreme conditions. The Downs, above the Isis, are notorious for their heavy snow. Many will recall the blizzards of 1947 and 1963, the intense cold of 1940 and the bitter wartime winters which followed.

Berkshire is far enough away from the rain that often fringes the Atlantic coast to share in some of the notable droughts. One of the worst was in 1921 when rainfall was on a par with that experienced at Alice Springs in the Australian desert. There was another drought in 1933, a year notorious for woodland fires, and who can possibly forget the wonderful summer of 1976 when, to save precious water, we were advised to bath with a friend!

There have been other weather phenomena in Berkshire — dust carried from the Sahara which has turned the countryside yellow, hailstones the size of golf balls, landslides and mudslides and smog along the industrial banks of the Thames.

The most capricious weather hazard of all is the radiation fog which occupies hollows, often hangs on hillsides and plagues M4 motorway drivers. It is most frequent during the long nights of early winter and has caused many motorway pile-ups.

BERKSHIRE'S HIGHS AND LOWS

WETTEST DAY
4.34 inches
(107.7mm)
on 12th July, 1901
at **Maidenhead**

WETTEST YEAR
47.12 inches
(1203mm)
at **Farnborough Rectory** in 1903

DRIEST MONTH
April 1912 was rainless at **Long Wittenham**. June 1925 was almost rainless in **Reading**. Very little rain fell during March 1929, September 1959 and October 1969.

DRIEST YEAR
12.87 inches
(327mm)
at **Bisham** in 1921

COLDEST DAY
-1.3F (-18.5C) on
14th January, 1982
at **Arborfield**

HOTTEST DAY
97.7F (36.5C) on
3rd August, 1990
at **Mortimer**

SNOWIEST WINTER
Letcombe Regis had snow cover for 62 days during 1963

SUNNIEST YEAR 1,854 hours at **Wokingham** in 1989

COLDEST WINTER The winter of 1962-3 was the coldest since 1740

Weather of long ago

A picture taken late in the nineteenth century of one of Berkshire's greatest survivors. The yew tree in the churchyard at Aldworth was reputed to be more than 1,000 years old and, despite its massive size, had withstood many raging blizzards and gales. It was to survive another 100 years before falling in the gale of 2nd January, 1976.

1595: Berkshire Chronicler Sidney Gilliham recorded in his diary full details of "the disastrous flooding of spring 1595" which followed a "black and bitter frost across the county." "My father took me walking," wrote Gilliham "and showed to me the bodies of beggars frozen to death besides the road. The dead bodies of birds fell from trees and foxes abandoned their wily ways and came into houses to be fed. The Thames was frozen, God knoweth how far to the west and to the east of Wallingford and beyond." The floods came with the thaw on 6th April and Gilliham wrote: "It took with it great toll of life, both human and cattle. It is said that more than one hundred were drowned and an hundred more dead of maladies brought by the waters. No such flood have I known since and I thank God for it. But this one I remember".

1795: On 14th February, workshops in Reading belonging to a Mr Billing fell into the swollen Kennet. His loss was estimated at £400.

The headboard in St Laurence's Churchyard, Reading tells the story. Henry West was a railwayman who perished in the whirlwind which struck the town on 24th March, 1840.

1810: This was the year that salmon, which had proliferated in the Thames, started to disappear. The reason was the invention of the flushing water closet and the fact that sewage was drained directly into the river. Later gas companies expelled their waste products into the Thames.

1813-14: One of Berkshire's most notorious winters. An iron frost froze over the Thames from bank to bank and heavy snow in the middle of January crippled everyday life. The mails to Reading were "greatly retarded" and the scenes around the county "were truly Canadian".

On 20th January, the Bristol and Bath downward mails were buried in the snow between Thatcham and the Turnpike and had to be dragged out by a team of horses. The mailbags were forwarded to Newbury in a cart and deposited with the postmaster.

1821: The Thames burst its banks in one of the worst floods of the nineteenth century.

1844: James Cornish who lived at Farringdon wrote: "A great drought lasted from 11th March to 23rd June and farmers had to cut boughs from the elm trees to feed their cattle."

1859: A great hailstorm with stones the size of pigeon's eggs battered windows at Windsor. Cattle were killed and trees stripped.

1860: An extremely cold Christmas. The mercury in the Wallingford area dropped to 0F (-18C).

Great feast on the frozen river

January, 1363

SHEEP roasting parties, frost fairs and skating have been a feature of many bitterly cold winters in Berkshire, for the Thames has frequently frozen over.

One of the earliest records was during the reign of King Edward III in 1363 when the Thames froze so thickly at Reading that the abbot ordained that all the poor and feeble of the town should be invited to a great feast on the river. First they needed sea-coal which was brought from Newcastle down the east coast and up the Thames as far as Maidenhead, where the ice prevented the passage of barges any further. Labour parties were organised to trundle the coal up the frozen river to the feast. It was then stacked in pyramids on the ice.

A contemporary report says that by nightfall, feast, coal and recipients had disappeared and nothing remained on the Thames but the stripped tables, the trestles that had held the hogshead of ale. Great fires had been lit on the banks of the river to keep the feasters warm and the monks from the abbey and brothers from Greyfriars had turned themselves into waiters for the occasion.

The fair on the frozen Thames in 1814

No more frost fairs on the Thames ?

THE great frost of 1683-4 was, historians tell us, the most severe ever known. Birds froze in mid-air, sheep and cattle died, country people suffered badly and trade was at a standstill. The Thames, of course, was frozen and the riverside inhabitants, particularly in London, enjoyed a carnival.

Great frosts also took place in 1776 and 1789. In 1776 it lasted from 7th January to 2nd February. Snow fell for 12 days and strong north-east winds piled it into drifts 13 feet deep. No news came through from Reading or Henley for 10 days. In 1789 the Thames was so entirely frozen that several people skated on it between Caversham Bridge and the Lock, a circumstance which had not occurred for many years.

There was a frost fair on the Thames in 1814 when immense masses of ice floated up the river and blocked Blackfriars and London Bridge. Two days later the river presented such a thoroughly solid surface that a fair was quickly organised and a great number of booths erected. By 2nd February the grand mall extended from Blackfriars to London Bridge.

Owing to the greatly changed geography of the Thames it was not feasible to hold frost fairs after 1895, when the last fair was held even though 1947 and 1963 were as cold as 1814.

Ice floes hinder King Charles on his final journey

IN January 1649, the Thames froze again and a disguised boat which was being secretly borne down the river from London to Windsor repeatedly encountered severe ice floes. In the boat was the decapitated body of Charles I who had just been beheaded for treason.

The small river party was "poled off" ice floes at Chertsey by local fishermen and was later challenged by Parliamentarians at Datchet. All the obstacles were evaded and in flurries of snow the secret hearse moored at Windsor and the coffin was borne up to the castle.

Hoar frost on 21st December, 1891 in the garden of The Mere, Upton, near Slough — the home of meteorologist Richard Bentley who had established his own weather station. Of this frost he wrote: "Even the grass grew nearly two inches in height and every tree had a different pattern of tracery. The weight supported was prodigious."

One of the highest Thames floods on record occurred in November 1852. It reached its climax on the 17th, the day before the state funeral of the Duke of Wellington at St Paul's Cathedral in London.

As the 'Iron Duke's' cortege made its way from his home in Hampshire through Berkshire, thousands braved the appalling weather to line the route. In Bath Road, Maidenhead, the hearse tipped over and the coffin fell into the swirling flood waters. Embarrassed that such an undignified event should happen to this great statesman and former Commander-in-chief of the British Army, the undertakers righted the coffin and proceeded with the journey to London.

There were no more mishaps. For more than two hours in London, tens of thousands of people stood by the roadside on the route to the Cathedral. It was made all the more moving by the respectful silence of the crowd. In Berkshire, the great inundation became known as the Duke of Wellington's Flood.

1868: A hot and dry summer with long spells of drought. There was only 0.07 inches of rain at Eton from 24th May to 21st June. No rain fell at all between 26th August and 18th September at Henley.

1870: A tornado on 19th October felled many trees in Swyncombe Gardens, Henley.

1875: Heavy rain between 10th and 14th November led to a rapid rise of the Thames with flooding at Maidenhead, Datchet, Eton and Windsor. Water came within one foot of the 1852 record. The Windsor racecourse was completely under water, only the grandstand being visible.

1879: Following a summer of "cloud and continuous rain", Britain suffered the worst harvest for decades. In Berkshire, farmers faced financial disaster. The situation was not helped by cheap American corn flooding the market.

1880: Another wet year. A weather observer at Long Wittenham, the Rev. Clutterbuck commented: "I have never before registered so many heavy falls of rain for 24 hours. There were six times when it was over an inch and rainfall amounted to 35.15 inches (898mm) for the year."

Two die as temperatures plunge to -2F

5th — 7th January, 1867

BERKSHIRE'S unofficial coldest day ever was 5th January, 1867 when the temperature at East Hendred dropped to -2F (-19C) — that's 34 degrees of frost. At Reading, 9F (-13C) was recorded. The great freeze came in the wake of an easterly wind which had whipped snow into huge drifts and halted all traffic on road and rail.

There were some extraordinary readings. At Cookham during the night of 4th and 5th January, the mercury was down to a numbing 7F (-14C). It was so cold that a woman, aged 78, died in her bed at Friar's Place, Reading and, at midnight, the switchman at Reading's Great Western Railway station was found frozen to death, 30 minutes after he went on duty.

Within 48 hours, the big freeze was just a memory. On 7th January, temperatures had climbed by 49 degrees to a spring-like 54F (12C).

When Henley's Bridge was 'swept to ruin'

On 12th March, 1774, the Thames, flooded by 12 successive days of rain, swept Henley's bridge to ruin. For many years to follow, post chaises and horse passengers were obliged to be ferried over and the passage of coaches entirely stopped. It was to be 12 years before a new bridge, designed by Mr William Hayward, was opened.

The 1774 floods caused considerable damage to the wharf at Newbury and, in Reading, a compting house belonging to a Mr Willis collapsed "due to the undermining of its foundations being carried away by the impetuosity of the current".

At Eaton Buttery this flood was higher by 4 inches than the 1894 floods which were to cause so much heartbreak (see page 22).

Berkshire prepares — the floods are imminent.

More bridges lost in another great flood

THE great Thames flood of 1809 was brought about by an extraordinary combination of weather events. On 19th January, heavy rain fell which immediately turned to ice. Every surface was covered by a thick layer of glaze onto which was deposited an enormous snowfall.

Three days later there was heavy rain which melted the snow but the water did not soak into the ground as that was still frozen. Instead, it poured into the rivers which produced a flood of disastrous proportions.

The central arch of Wallingford Bridge was swept away. Water reached as high as parlour windows and many poor people "lost their all". At Preston Crowmarsh, the flood mark was almost two feet higher than the infamous 1894 floods. At Windsor, the Eton Bridge was carried away and the fifteenth arch of the Eton to Slough Bridge capsized due to the violence of the surging waters. The people of Bisham also lost their Green Bridge and "there was no churching on the following Sunday as the water was so high".

Henley, 10th June, 1829

A competition between Britain's two senior universities to establish the superiority of one over the other at rowing was held on a dull, rather cold day at Henley. Cambridge wore pink sashes round woolly vests but their choice of a cheerful colour on a cheerless day brought them no luck. Oxford, favouring their sombre dark blue, won.

This first university boat race was full of incident. The teams started off from Hambleden Lock but half way through the race the boats collided, so they started again. They paddled back to the starting point, then for 2 miles they rowed upstream in primitive eight oars with keels. The seats were fixed and there were no outriggers, so it was one mighty struggle.

The president of Cambridge, whose name was Snow, immediately put out a challenge for a repeat performance the following year. In fact, it did not take place until 1836 when the course was from Westminster to Putney.

1883: Due to the eruption of Mount Krakatoa in the Sunda Straits between Java and Sumatra on 27th August, the autumn was remarkable for a peculiar rich and radiating glow in the sky an hour either side of sunset. This was due to volcanic dust shot into the atmosphere.

1884: A very dry year. At Wallingford only 17.86 inches (456mm) fell. The Lambourn river ceased running on 13th October and it remained completely dry for some time. Several wells failed.

1888: At Shrivenham snow fell for 24 hours on 13th and 14th February. It measured two feet. At Lambourn a depth of 19 inches was recorded. Several people travelling between Wallingford and the neighbouring villages lost their way in the blizzard. Snow was still visible on hills as late as 13th April. A month's rainfall fell in two hours during a storm at Little Wittenham on 30th July. So great was the deluge (2.95 inches or 75 mm) that the equivalent of 50 cart-loads of earth and stones had been washed to the bottom of one field of potatoes.

JOLLY BOATING WEATHER

ON those balmy summer days in the late nineteenth century, the "young gentlemen" of Eton College frequently donned their blazers and straw hats, bought a hamper from Fortnums and, with their portable "harmonium" in their pocket, took the girls punting from Windsor to Cliveden. The habit spawned a well-known sonnet — The Eton Boating Song.

Maidenhead, with its shingly riverbed and many shady trees, was always the best spot for punting and every summer weekend, the strains of the song could be picked up by those walking on the banks. There was one unwritten rule. When passing each other the boys would take off their boaters and screen their faces and the girls would do the same with their parasols. This was the gentlemanly game of complete ignorance of identity.

The regatta at Henley in 1891

King Sol smiles on Henley's Regatta

ON a wonderfully balmy June day in 1839, the town of Henley organised a regatta, which the townsfolk hoped would become an annual event. It did. From that day there has been an annual succession of regatta parties in all degrees of social distinction and all kinds of weather.

The regatta in 1867 was also blessed with good weather and Hone's Everyday book records the occasion: "The grace of the ladies and the dignity of the gentlemen and the endurance of the competitors has been noteworthy. Parasols, laces and ribbons and furbelows of every variety, uniforms, swords, elegant cravats and all the sartorial modes of the day have been evident on every hand. Our Fatherly Thames has flowed softly in sylvan beauty down the reach, his gentle ripples cleft by the boats and rhythmically agitated by the oarsmen, and each day

King Sol had smiled his benifice."

Hone had different things to say about the events of the evening. "Each night has seen ruder activities. We mean the customary onset of intoxication that the lower orders in particular seem to delight in, though many of them are forever seeking charity. It is scarcely to the advantage of a Royal Occasion that this year the beauty of the Thames has been sullied by riotous bands of rough men (and a few of the gentler sex) who make no ado about throwing each other bodily into the water in search of coolth when they are overheated by grape and grain."

Today, of course, Henley is in Oxfordshire but the Berkshire bank claims a full share of these time-honoured proceedings — and no-one seems to care when a party-goer seeks the solace of a river recovery!

The waterspout at Maidenhead in June 1853

Whirl of water spirals over Maidenhead

14th June, 1853

THE sketch of a waterspout in Maidenhead was published in the Illustrated London News of 2nd July, 1853 accompanied by a description of the phenomenon which was seen by scores of people.

A correspondent, Mr E.E. Kay wrote to the magazine. "A June shower had just abated when my attention was drawn to the appearance of a vast whirl of water about a quarter of a mile in length. It did not touch the ground but gradually diminished to a point at about 60 to 80 feet above it, and seemed to be trailed along in a wavy shape by the progress of the cloud to which it was attached — just like a pennon on a calm day would float from the mast of a steamer in slow motion.

"The tube-like formation of the water was clearly apparent and the whole of its surface was in most

rapid circular or spiral motion. The waterspout appeared to be a few hundred yards distant from me and eventually detached itself from the cloud and so remained whirling around by itself. In insensible degrees it then dissipated."

Mr Kay said the air was still and there was no commotion underneath where the spout appeared to terminate. It was accompanied by slight flashes of lightning and low thunder. "When the waterspout disappeared", said Mr Kay, "the rain fell tremendously from that part of the cloud to which the spout had been attached. Soon afterwards, the rain ceased and the evening was fair and calm."

The writer made his sketch by memory and explained that he had seen waterspouts at sea and elsewhere, but none which presented such an extraordinary appearance. The accuracy of the sketch was testified by five people who also witnessed the Maidenhead phenomenon.

Three men in a boat in the land of vain regrets

IN the summer of 1888, three young men, George, Harris and Jerome, set off to row the stretch of the Thames between Oxford and Kingston. Their object was to idle away the long summer days surrounded by the calm waters of the river and the pleasant rolling countryside. The Berkshire weather turned their journey into a nightmare!

One of the voyagers, Jerome K Jerome, wrote a whimsical book about the adventure. It was called *Three Men in a Boat* and was an instant success, soon earning a place as one of the literary masterpieces of the century.

Describing the weather on the Thames he wrote: "The river — chill and weary, with the ceaseless raindrops falling on its brown and sluggish waters, with the sound as of a woman, weeping low as in some dark chamber, while the woods, all dark and silent, shrouded in their mists of vapour, stand like ghosts upon the margin; silent ghosts with eyes reproachful, like the ghosts of evil actions, like the ghosts of friends neglected — is a spirit-haunted water through the land of vain regrets".

After enduring this depressing weather for two days during their journey downstream, Jerome, Harris and George abandoned their trip at Pangbourne, near Reading and caught a train to London.

The scene in Northcroft Lane, Newbury in February 1883.

Newbury firemen in canoes

FEBRUARY 1883 was one of the wettest months of the century. During the weekend of 11th to 13th the rain fell out of the sky with a tropical intensity and without respite. In Newbury, the River Kennet could not cope; the banks burst and flood waters raced through the town. On the Monday, firemen "disported themselves in canoes in West Street" and by Tuesday Northbrook Street had experienced such severe flooding that a trench was dug across the street to Alton Place (Park Street) to allow the water to drain into the Marsh (Victoria Street).

The River Lambourn also overflowed at Shaw and the view westwards from the parish church tower was as of one large lake.

Previous big floods in Newbury had occurred in 1814 and 1871, but the 1883 inundation was believed to have been worse. The picture above shows Northcroft Lane, Newbury. On the left is Drummers Beerhouse. Ironically, the premises next door was the Temperance Hall.

■ On 12th March, 1876 the Empress of Austria, travelling from Windsor on the royal train, was caught in a snowstorm and stranded at Slough for many hours. The telegraph wires had become coated by ice until the weight was too great for the supports and they crashed onto the railway line along with miles and miles of entangled wires.

Trains buried in raging blizzard

18th January, 1881

THE snowstorm of Tuesday 18th January, 1881 was among the greatest on record in southern England. Piercing easterly winds accompanied by a massive fall of fine, powder-like snow, whipped up drifts in excess of 15 feet in places and the fine ice crystals were blasted through the smallest of cracks into people's homes. Everyday life in towns and villages was crippled and many trains were completely buried, sometimes containing their passengers. Around the county several people were found frozen to death.

A spell of intense frost which froze over Berkshire's rivers and lakes preceded the blizzard which raged for at least 36 hours.

The scene in Newbury was typical of that in all Berkshire towns. Many shopkeepers kept up their shutters all day, the town "presenting a most winterly and forsaken appearance". The *Newbury Herald* said the driving snow "was well nigh blinding and all who could possibly avoid encountering the storm naturally did so".

In many parts of Newbury the snow drifted to depths of 10 to 12 feet and a train became marooned in the cutting near Savernake. Most business was suspended The mails could not be sent by any kind of vehicle, so bad was the state of the roads and all telegraph services were clogged with people trying to send messages to the outside world.

The services of 100 navvies were offered to clear the Great Western Railway but GWR officials eventually succeeded in clearing a passage themselves. At Goring, a railwayman was killed during the storm when he underestimated the width of a train while clearing the line. Some of the carriages of a train where he was digging were covered with six feet of frozen snow.

A man and a boy, together with three horses were all frozen to death while out in the blizzard on the Lambourn Downs. They had hauled several cart-loads of coal to Lambourn, a distance of 10 miles, but on their return faced the full severity of the weather and, in the blinding snow, became completely lost on the Downs for several hours before perishing.

There were other fatalities on this bitter day. A groom near Shrivenham died of the cold while driving to the station in a conveyance. A 40-year-old man, leading two horses through the snow at Cold Ash became totally exhausted and died from severe exposure. A young woman was so feeble with cold after being carried over the field on the back of her male friend that her companion had to lie her down by the roadside and run for assistance. On his return she was dead. At Inkpen, a carter collapsed yards from his cottage. He tried to crawl to safety but failed to reach home before the cold claimed him. A labourer, aged 19, was found dead in the snow at Chilton, near Abingdon.

In many parts of Abingdon, the snow was up to six feet deep. One man who was driving to the town lost his pony when it "just disappeared into a ditch". He dragged the animal free and headed on through snow that was breast deep. They were rescued by search teams carrying lanterns and spades.

Near Wantage, an elderly crippled man who travelled to and from work on a donkey succumbed to the cold during the height of the snowstorm. The donkey stood next to his body for two days. He was found by a search party from Kingston Lisle.

The scene at Radley Station on that Tuesday night belied belief. No less than five trains, carrying 300 passengers, came to a standstill and, as there were only two or three houses nearby, the passengers were compelled to make do with what shelter they could find. Next day, after several hours' work, the Radley road from Abingdon to the station was cleared to allow vans and carts to squeeze through with provisions for the beleaguered passengers. On that infamous Wednesday, many were taken to Abingdon and given accommodation. An attempt was made later to force an engine, containing provisions, from Oxford to Radley but it ran off the rails and the food had to be carried the rest of the way on foot. Drifts on the line were so severe that many passengers had to spend another night at Radley Station.

There were similar dramas all round the county. 100 passengers were trapped for 14 hours on the Didcot to London express when it became buried in snow in the Moreton Cutting. Scores of navvies worked untiringly to reach the passengers who were returned to Didcot and put up in hotels with "inadequate food". In parts of Wallingford, the snow had piled up to 18 feet and a train became embedded one mile from the station.

Poor and needy inhabitants of Newbury were handed soup and bread after an appeal by the mayor. On Friday 21st January, "300 gallons were distributed at the Municipal Buildings and the next day, 200 gallons were served at the Corn Exchange."

For some, it was fun. Skaters flocked to the Kennet and Avon Canal which was covered with ice, and there were excellent conditions at Benham Park and

A crowd gathers outside the Bush Hotel. A rare photograph of Reading in January 1881.

Sandleford. Other favourite locations for skaters were Ditton Park and Virginia Water.

Tragedies, however, continued to mount. A labourer was found dead from the cold behind the Lord Nelson Inn, Old Windsor and a serious train accident occurred when locomotives used by clearance gangs collided at Datchet. One of the men had his ribs and jaw broken and two others were less seriously injured. Trains were snowed up at Wraysbury and Ascot.

The *Reading Mercury* described the blizzard as "memorable in the annals of meteorology for the county had been left in a state of utter helplessness." Before the snowstorm started, the temperature had plunged to 2F (-17C) or 30 degrees of frost.   The

blizzard caused "three-fourths of Reading's shops to close and hundreds of stranded train passengers were forced to cram into the town's pubs and hotels, while the poorer classes shivered in the poorly heated waiting rooms."

Hungerford, like many towns, was isolated for two days. At Henley, the Thames was frozen but skaters found the going tough and chose to partake of their favourite sport at Twyford where the meadows afforded plenty of frozen surfaces.

It was nine days after the blizzard that the thaw arrived. Henley was enshrouded in a thick fog as the milder air passed over the wintry landscape.

The Swan Inn at Pangbourne, possibly seen during the winter of 1881.

Golden Jubilee celebrations at Abingdon on 21st June, 1887. Umbrellas were out to protect the delicate complexions of Victorian ladies from the sun's rays. In the centre is a huge white statue of Her Majesty.

Bank Holiday Monday introduced as an additional day off for the first time in 1871, always brought the cheerful hordes to the banks of the Thames. The wonderful August of 1885 was no exception and Cookham Lock was especially popular. This was a year of very little rain in which the grass suffered badly. Then, suddenly, it was too wet and the grass in the autumn was destroyed by grubs.

Jubilee Day, 1897 at Wallingford

Berkshire blessed with Queen's weather

21st June, 1897

THE fiftieth anniversary of the reign of Queen Empress Victoria was blessed with wonderful weather, but what would be in store for the sixtieth? Queen's weather once more was too much to hope for! As the big day — 21st June, 1897 — drew near, the weather in Berkshire was gloomy with heavy rain, high winds and a falling barometer. There was little doubt that the greatest celebration the county had ever planned was on course to compete with the weather.

"Providence smiled." wrote the *Reading Mercury* . "The Monarch, whose chief residence is in our midst, and who has so wisely administered the affairs of the mightiest empire in the world, enjoyed a day of brilliant sunshine. It was Queen's weather. The June sun looked down from the heavens in unclouded glory from dawn to setting."

And the *Berkshire Chronicle* said: "As the Queen was leaving Buckingham Palace on her path of triumph the sun blessed the occasion with undiminished splendour everywhere, until the going down thereof."

This was certainly one of the greatest days in British history. Celebrations were held in every hamlet, village and town but it was Windsor which excelled in the extent of its decoration and ceremonial pageantry. "This was only fitting", said the *Mercury,* "for the Queen has always shown herself so gracious to the people she delights to honour."

At a special service at St Laurence's Church, the Bishop of Reading said: "During her great reign the Empire has grown and to it has been added a new world in a distant ocean. There has been the triumph of science, the onward march of art, the progress of material welfare, the development of resources and the unexpected activity of invention".

Little wonder that Royal Berkshire wanted to celebrate.

1890 — 1900

1890: This was the coldest December of the century with a frost every day at Maidenhead. The temperature did not rise above 21F (-6C) at Reading on the 14th during 11 successive days below freezing.

1891: An exceptionally dry February was followed by severe snowdrifts on 9th March. Whitsuntide too, was bedevilled by unseasonable cold with squalls of snow and hail on 17th and 18th May. October was disastrously wet for farmers.

1892: A chilly winter and frosty March meant little in the way of vegetation by the end of the month. The year ended with another cold December, a feature of this period.

1893: During the greatest spring drought of the century the only rain that fell at Farringdon between 3rd March and 11th May was caused by mist or dew. There was a heatwave between 8th and 19th August and a violent gale from 16th to 20th November with heavy snow.

1894: On the 26 days between 23rd October and 17th November, more than eight inches (200 mm) of rain fell in the Thames Valley amounting to 440,000 million gallons. The floods were worse than those of 1852 with hundreds of families forced to abandon their homes.

1895: One of the coldest Februarys of the 19th century with temperatures falling to 2F (minus 17C) but very dry. Newbury was almost rainless with only 0.15 inches (4 mm). It was an extremely dry first half of the year with only 6.77 inches (172 mm) to the end of June but 17.85 inches (456 mm) in the second half, at Reading.

1896: At Long Wittenham it was a dry year up to 19th August but from then to the middle of October, 10.5 inches (268 mm) of rain fell.

1897: This year was the opposite to the preceding year, being wet until Queen Victoria's Diamond Jubilee . On 24th June there was a violent storm in Maidenhead with considerable marble sized hail. Rain and melted hail amounted to nearly an inch in just 30 minutes.

There was a novel scene on 8th February at Summerlea Farm in Maidenhead. Despite deep floods a local farmer went ahead with his farmstock auction while those attending had to proceed in punts through acres of water. Although the sale was on land above the flood level, a good deal of the tools were under water and thus invisible! According to the *Morning Advertiser* never had a farm sale been carried out in such bizarre circumstances.

1898: A very dry year with only 17.26 inches (441mm) falling at Windsor, eight inches below average. At Ascot, wells failed for the first time in living memory. September was particularly warm by day with the mercury rising to over 80 F (27C) on nine days at Sunninghill. The prolonged dry weather killed many old trees in Windsor Great Forest.

1899: A fine summer which exceeded 80F (27C) on 12 days during July.

Henley in November, 1894 one of the greatest floods ever known.

"Dandelions in great profusion everywhere"

Berkshire farmers at their wits end during...

Writing of the 1893 drought, Mr James Cornish who lived at Faringdon said: "It was terrible. No measurable rain fell from 28th February to 16th May and by the end of April the grass, even in the Thames-side meadows, was brown and dandelions in great profusion everywhere. Old inhabitants said there had not been such a dry spring since 1844.

"In 1893 we had a brief respite of rain in May but, in early June, the great heat returned and all through the summer the farmers were at their wit's end to find food for the animals. Hay cost £7 a ton and there was little to be had, even at that price. I was told of one farmer who offered his flock of sheep to a neighbour at 5s a piece but was refused. One never saw the cows lying down. They were always walking about in search of food. July was also dry, the corn was thin and stunted and the root crops a complete failure. It was

West Ilsley on the Berkshire Downs probably taken in the remarkable spring/early summer of 1893.

...the greatest spring drought of the century

terrible."

The period between late February and mid May provided the greatest spring drought of the century and on the Berkshire Downs below the Isis all the water had been absorbed by the vast chalk sponge.

Faringdon, Great Coxwell, Coleshill, Hatford and Pusey suffered badly and even the famous well in the village of Buscot was virtually dry. It was the same story in West Ilsley, a lonely village

high on the Downs, which once boasted two breweries. In the spring of 1893 the inhabitants had little water and no beer.

So bad was the situation that a "dowser" was employed to find a spring that hadn't failed. His tour of the area cost thousands of pounds and there were angry letters to the local newspapers condemning the "folly of following a man with a twisting stick".

Eton head swims for his life

13th — 17th November, 1894

THE November floods of 1894 were so spectacular, so catastrophic and so widespread that they were to take a place in Berkshire's folklore as the greatest floods ever and the yardstick by which all future inundations in the county would be measured.

At the time, however, the scale of the disaster and its likely historic implications was of no compensation to the people who were made homeless or lost their jobs when the Thames burst its banks and invaded scores of towns, villages, hamlets and farmsteads. Thousands were affected by the 1894 floods but no-one had a better reason to remember them than the headmaster of Eton College and his 1,000 students.

On Saturday 17th November, Dr Warre found the only way he could get to the school was by a punt along the Slough Road. The craft became fixed in some bushes and Dr Warre was thrown into the swirling, muddy waters. He was rescued, but decided the conditions were so bad that his pupils should be sent home. That was his second mistake. Delighted by the news of their surprise holiday, students charged to the Windsor post office to telegraph their parents and in the ensuing stampede several staff were lucky to avoid injury.

It was in the early hours of 13th November that a few spots of rain pattered gently across the valleys of Berkshire, gradually increasing in tempo until they became a deluge of ferocious intensity. The rivers could not cope with the sheer weight and speed of the water. Along the great winding course of the Thames and its tributaries — the Kennet, Loddon, Lambourn and Blackwater — flood defences capitulated and new lakes were created. Chroniclers quickly dubbed the 1894 floods as "the worst in living memory". They were probably right.

In Reading, more than 6,000 men were driven from their work by the rapid rise of the Thames and the Kennet. During Wednesday and Thursday the advance of the water was so incessant that many people just packed a few belongings and abandoned their homes. Others carried household goods to upper storeys and watched in dismay as the brown waters rose higher and higher.

The enlarged river engulfed the Huntley and Palmer biscuit factory at Reading, extinguishing the furnaces and throwing 4,000 hands out of employment. It then attacked the malthouses of Messrs Simonds, the brewers, the timber wharf of Messrs Ridley, the saw mill of Geo. Lewis, the bicycle factory of Mr Warrick and the Great Western Ironworks. The *Reading Mercury* described the event in vivid detail.

"The village of Coley", they wrote, "is a most melancholy spectacle. The furious storm turned the Holy Brook into a destructive mass of swirling water in which floated cattle and pigs from Fobney Meadows." Towards Caversham, the conditions were even worse. "All the houses are flooded to a lamentable extent and planks and boats are the only means whereby the occupants can get to and from their houses. The road from Reading to Caversham is impassable."

The Great Western Railway suffered badly. At Sonning Cutting a landslip carried away a large piece of the embankment, at Bedwyn, the line was impassable, at Savernake and Mortimer, huge masses of earth blocked the metals.

In Henley, the Little White Hart and waterside homes were flooded to a depth of several feet and roads in the town were impassable. On Thursday morning (15th) two young men in a boat were attempting to reach a cottage near the New Mills. Their boat capsized and was smashed to pieces and the men were hurtled down the "rapids" but somehow survived.

The Vale of Kennet was a remarkable sight. Aldermaston, Theale, Lower Burghford resembled a huge sea of mud. In fields a long way from the river, water swished around the bellies of grazing cattle which had to be rescued by riders on horseback. Ashampstead, a village which had suffered so badly in the 1893 drought, was hardly recognisable and at the New Inn horses were submerged up to their girths.

It was the same damp story in the Swallowfield district where the River Blackwater invaded thousands of acres, the Loddon valley where customers of the George Hotel had to be ferried to and fro in boats and Twyford, where the "waters were unparalleled for extent and depth".

At Maidenhead, the force of the water on the Thames was terrific. A bridge, known as the Moor Arches, collapsed and a man who was sitting on the coping sustained severe injuries. Animal carcasses were swept under Maidenhead bridge and, at the height of the floods to the alarm of those who dared to watch, four human bodies were seen to be carried away at a tremendous rate. "The water", said the *Maidenhead Advertiser*, "attained such proportions that it exceeded even that of the memorable flood of 1852."

The same comparison was made in Windsor where "immense loss was occasioned to hundreds of residents". The Windsor Royal Gas Light Company

announced they would be unable to make gas and the Windsor Corporation pleaded with inhabitants to reduce their consumption of water and to boil that used for drinking purposes.

On Saturday afternoon (17th November), Queen Victoria left Windsor Castle to inspect the floods in Home Park and Datchet. She was accompanied by Prince Christian Victor and Princess Victoria of Schleswig-Holstein. The presence of the royal party and the spectacular sight of the inundations attracted thousands of people to the Castle terrace.

Throughout Berkshire, flood relief parties were

The innkeeper of the George Hotel, Pangbourne and customers during the floods of 1894.

quickly organised, coal and bread conveyed in punts and rafts to the homes of the sufferers and an appeal for funds opened in every community. Her Majesty gave £50 to the Windsor fund. She also ordered large quantities of soup to be made in the royal kitchens and distributed to the poor.

A few lives were lost in the 1894 floods and personal distress was caused on a scale never known before. It took many weeks for the waters to subside.

Caversham Road, Reading provided another bizarre spectacle.

Punting to the rescue in the village of Cookham during the great floods of November 1894.

The floods at Slough, as seen from the garden of Richard Bentley's home at Upton.

The flooded railway line at Kennington Junction in November 1894.

The Ark greeted its customers two by two as the water in Maidenhead continued to rise!

The Thames shows two of its many moods — the rising torrent at Henley in November 1894 and the frozen weir at Pangbourne two months later in January 1895.

Skating on the Thames at Abingdon Lock in the icy winter of 1895.

Abingdon Lock in 1895. In this early photograph the subjects have obviously been told to hold the pose. In this bitterly cold winter the Wilts and Berks canal froze over completely and it was possible to skate from Abingdon to Swindon. Although 100 years old, the canal's usefulness was waning owing to the arrival of the railway to Berkshire in 1841. By 1897 the canal had been abandoned and in 1914 the water from it was drained.

THE penetrating frost and the intense cold of both January and February 1895 caused the Thames to freeze, welding boats to the ice for many weeks. It also led to the cancellation of football matches and put hundreds of people out of work. Soup kitchens were set up to alleviate the distress of the hungry and funds opened to help the poor. The better-off enjoyed perfect conditions for skating.

The cold spell began at the end of January when high pressure over the Continent fed bitterly cold air over England. From 5th to 12th February, the temperature in much of Berkshire failed to climb above freezing point day and night.

At Reading, the ice which formed on the waterwork filters exceeded nine inches in thickness and the water supply failed. There were 250 fractures in the four-inch mains, 665 fractures in the three-inch mains and 560 service pipes had to be repaired. At Oxford a coach ventured onto the frozen Thames and throngs of people walked onto the ice. The Kennet and Avon Canal was closed for one month because of the severe frost, and an ice boat was provided by GWR with a regular trader providing the haulage for it.

This picture of Twyford, although undated, could have been taken in the winter of 1895.

The summer of 1898 was so dry that many wells failed for the first time in living memory. The sun blessed two royal occasions — the Queen's visit to Wantage (above) and the Henley Regatta in July.

1900 — 1909

Reading recreation ground flooded in June 1903

1900: Heavy snow nearly eight inches deep fell on the night of 2nd February in the Cookham area. This was followed by a quick thaw and rain on 17th which led to widespread floods.

In April the temperature rose to 70F (21C) on 21st, a brief precursor to a hot July where, in the Windsor district, the mercury exceeded 80F (27C) for more than half the month.

Autumn was dry and elms suffered from the drought in stark contrast to February.

On 11th and 12th June severe hailstorms in first Wallingford and then Wantage and Abingdon, caused considerable damage.

1901: Winter was rather late in arriving with thick snow, nine inches deep in the Bracknell area, on 4th February. It was a dry year with only 18.29 inches (467 mm) of rain measured at Windsor. However, there was a remarkable thunderstorm which gave 4.24 inches (108.3mm) of rain at Maidenhead and Lowood, the county record for one day, and there was considerable damage from lightning and flooding; almost 4inches (92 mm) of rain fell in an hour.

1902: A Mr Maker, an observer at Yattendon Court, wrote of this year: "The season early in the year was one of great promise but a cold spring, a dull sunless summer and a wet August put paid to it. At Sunninghill, Ascot 4 inches (100mm) of rain was recorded in June and more than 4 inches during the month of August.

1903: In a somewhat mild winter there was a brief cold spell with excellent skating on 13th January but February was exceedingly mild. It was a wet year with an observer at Warfield exclaiming, "the rain in

June and October was like a tropical downpour and the land at the end of the year was quite sodden. In June a 72-hour deluge brought 3.69 inches (94 mm) to Cookham and the Thames rose to 4ft 2in above headwater level producing a serious inundation of low-lying ground. At Sunningdale, on five occasions, more than an inch of rain fell in 24 hours and throughout the Thames Valley it was the wettest year then recorded. Farnborough Rectory measured 47.12 inches.

1904: At Newbury rainfall for January and February amounted to 8.37 inches (214 mm). The Thames rose 4ft 6ins above high water level. At Romney levels were a foot higher than in 1903 but less than 1894. The Mayor of Maidenhead wrote to *The Times* purporting that the floods actually did the health of Maidenhead good, counteracting press reports to the contrary.

The year ended with a prolonged fog, often dense, which lasted for ten days from 18th December.

1905: "Ne'er cast a clout 'til May be out", was a wise saying this year for on 22nd and 23rd temperatures plunged below freezing. Severe frosts returned remarkably early in the season with the temperature as low as 18F (-8C) at Wantage on 22nd October.

A vivid display of the aurora, blood red and crimson, could be seen from many parts of England between 6.20 and 8.30pm on 15th December.

1906: Four men were struck by lightning while sheltering in a shed during a thunderstorm at Emmer Green, Reading. A heatwave in late August to early September caused an early leaf fall, the foliage on trees quickly turning brown as no rain fell for nearly three weeks. At Maidenhead the mercury almost touched 95F (35C) on the last day of August. Only 2.63 inches of rain (67 mm) was measured during July, August and September at Newbury. Late on Christmas evening it started snowing and by dawn on Boxing Day snow lay four inches deep across much of Berkshire, the century's first White Christmas.

1907: An unseasonably cold Whitsuntide (20th May). "Within recent years the festival has been so well favoured in the matter of weather", so wrote *The Times*, "that one has almost forgotton the time when a run of bad seasons led to the use of the cheap sobriquet 'Wet Monday'. June was particularly cool, making the need for winter clothing necessary. Temperatures rose to only the mid fifties Fahrenheit and the rest of the summer was not much better. A violent storm battered Abingdon on 22nd July with 2.25 inches (57 mm)of rain and it was not until 25th September that the temperature reached the high seventies.

The water carrier collects what he can from a pond that is in danger of drying up. This picture could have been taken in 1906 when no rain fell for almost three weeks, but it is more likely to have been in the very dry year of 1898, when wells failed.

1908: April is often an uncertain month and none more so than this year as an almost unprecedented snowfall began around 4am on 25th and continued all day, reaching an undrifted 27 inches at Abingdon. This caused extensive damage throughout the county, many bees were destroyed at Yattendon and bemused swallows were seen flying around Newbury Bridge at the height of the snow storm. Following the Great January Blizzard of 1881 a law had been introduced, demanding that householders clear snow from their frontages. Failure to do so resulted in a visit from the police.

A late heatwave sent temperatures soaring to 82F (28C) on 1st October at Maidenhead, but there was an early taste of winter when the mercury fell to 10F (-12C) on 10th November at Wokingham. The year ended with another thick snowstorm and daytime temperatures below 23F (-5C) on 30th December.

1909: Mr Betteridge of Steventon accurately summed up this year from a farmer's standpoint. "It was the most wretched season since 1879. March had almost incessant rain, June and July were provokingly showery and from August to October it was very wet and in some cases harvest was impossible." However, remarkable May sunshine lasted 306 hours.

June 1902 and Maidenhead is flooded again, after a deluge which produced more than four inches of rain. The people of the town didn't seem unduly perturbed as they went about their everyday business, on foot and by punt.

The people of Berkshire, experienced one of the wettest years ever recorded in 1903. The Thames Valley suffered badly. In June the river rose to 4ft 2inches above headwater level and there were serious inundations everywhere. Maidenhead, of course, was one of the first to "go under".

This gatekeeper at Cookham Dean on 13th April, 1900 kept his great-coat well buttoned up against cold and stormy weather. By 21st of the month, however, the temperature had risen to 70F(21C).

At last a summer worth waiting for. It was mostly dry, although slightly chilly in June, but in August 1906 there was a heatwave and the thermometer climbed into the nineties and the hot spell lasted till early September. In these conditions the East Ilsley sheep fair, once the largest in England outside London, was especially popular. It started on the Wednesday in Easter week and went on every alternate Wednesday throughout the summer; in fact the fortunes of the village were founded on the sheep market. In 1906 the sheep sales were still of great importance but not for much longer; refrigerated ships could bring in massive quantities of cheaper lamb and mutton from Australia and New Zealand and that killed the market for home-reared meat. By the end of the twentieth century, East Ilsley's premier business was the training of racehorses.

'Button to chin, 'til May be in'

April snowstorm of 1908

APRIL can have all the seasons of the year rolled into one and is often the most fickle. Shakespeare wrote of "the uncertain glory of an April day" and these words rang true in the latter half of April, 1908 when a snowstorm buried the county in such a deep, icy blanket as had seldom been experienced, even in the strongest grip of the most severe winter.

The culprit was a depression, an area of low pressure, which moved south-eastwards from Ireland to the English Channel and then ran slowly north-east over the Thames estuary. Berkshire lay on its northern flank in the cold air and snow began at around 5am on Saturday 25th and continued unabated at a prodigious rate until half past seven at night. The snowfall was particularly heavy in the west and not since the Great Blizzard of January, 1881 had such snow been seen. Newbury all but came to a standstill, the streets were deserted and shops closed.

At Kingsclere a Dr Maples took a yard measure and went with difficulty into the middle of his meadow to ascertain the depth of this truly remarkable downfall of snow. Having inserted it perpendicularly it still did not touch the earth. At Bucklebury, men sought shelter quite exhausted and brewers' drays were left beside the road. On Sunday, bakers' carts could not negotiate huge drifts and it was not until late in the day that some intrepid delivery men made it through, much to the delight of the isolated families.

At Hamstead Norreys, not even the oldest residents could remember such a fall so late in the year. With two feet of snow on the ground it was useless to hold a service in the parish church. In Peasemore, high on the Downs, conditions were appalling, with drifts five feet deep, and a rescue party of six sturdy villagers and three horses set out to look for several missing carriers. After trudging through waist-deep snow, they were located at Chieveley and were fortified with some "home brewed parsnip", famous at Peasemore.

The snow fell with such thickness it brought "white-out" conditions. This was dramatically illustrated by a tragic event at Compton when a group of men with four horses were crossing the railway line at Roden Farm when a train suddenly rushed out of the blinding snow and hit a horse, killing it instantly, though the men miraculously escaped.

At Abingdon, business was at a standstill with snow on some of the streets reaching three feet in depth, whilst near Lambourn the railway cutting at Eastbury was blocked and passengers had to wait forlornly in the snowbound train as gangs of workmen cleared the line. A horse and trap belonging to Mr Wells the butcher became stuck fast in huge drifts at East Garston, the trap being abandoned.

The sheer weight of snow brought down various glass roofs and verandahs and the roofs of some old buildings gave way at Whitchurch. The snow was so deep in Newbury that one lady recalled that when she returned home to Howard Road from work that day, she was unable to find her garden gate. Another lady remembered taking her husband's dinner to him, as he ran a butcher's stall in the Market Place. It was a terrible journey from Kings Road, Newbury. She slipped and slithered many times and the snow came completely over her gumboots. At the height of the storm a confused swallow was seen flying around Newbury Bridge.

A bye-law had decreed after the 1881 snowstorm that householders had to clear the snow from their frontages and it was enforced. Those that did not comply were visited by the police on Sunday morning and instructed to do so. Meanwhile, stranded rail passengers at Newbury were inquiring who would foot the bill for an over-night stay.

It was a similar story at Hungerford. The mail coach from Swindon was abandoned on Saturday night and there was no delivery until Sunday afternoon.

But, such is the caprice of April's weather that the sun shone on Sunday and a rapid thaw set in, turning the snow-laden streets into water courses and by 29th the mercury reached as high as 62F, with virtually all traces of snow having disappeared, although rivers were in high flood, with many houses inundated in Maidenhead.

Newbury in April, 1908

THE BLIZZARD APRIL 25 08

Trinity Church, Abingdon on 25th April, 1908.

Clearing the footpaths at Wallingford on the same day.

Slow progress for this horse and cart along Wokingham Road, Reading in April, 1908.

The great spring snowstorm lasted 16 hours. This was the scene at Newbury the following day.

Cookham Rise in the 'springtime' of 1908.

After the snow came the floods. This was Wargrave on 29th April, 1908.

A cyclist faces a sea of melting hail in Beresford Road, Reading, 9th June, 1910.

Fury of the summer storm

9th June, 1910

THE scene in Reading, Caversham and the surrounding villages on a sultry June morning in 1910 was astonishing. A storm had unleashed so many hailstones that the appearance of the streets suggested a great fall of snow. The stones were more than half an inch in diameter and the force of them smashed hundreds of panes of glass. Chimney pots were damaged, shops and homes flooded and nursery plants ruined.

The *Berkshire Chronicle* said the great heat of 9th June was the precursor to the storm. "Just before midday, a general darkness prevailed — darkness that was periodically relieved by vivid and alarming flashes of lightning. Caversham primary school was hit, so terrifying school children that four of them fainted. One of the teachers, Miss Smee, was watching the storm when suddenly there was a great flash and the upper part of her body appeared to be paralysed. Her arm was badly blistered and she was unable to speak for some time."

Lightning also struck the telegraph instrument at Caversham post office and The Rookery in Conisborough Avenue. Other flashes knocked a man off his bike, killed a bullock and toppled a chimney pot where chimney sweep, John Soper, was working below. "He was so badly shocked", said the *Chronicle*, "that he had to remain in bed for two days."

1910 — 1919

Oxford Road, Reading on 9th June, 1910

1910: On 25th April, Reading received the most prolonged hailstorm for many years, inflicting great damage to fruit trees. June brought a thundery spell with severe storms on 7th when over 2.2 inches (56 mm) fell in just 90 minutes at Beaumont College, Windsor. Lightning tore up the ground in fields near Wantage, buildings caught fire and sheep were killed. On 9th great devastation was wrought on Reading by another series of thunderstorms. One horticulturist alone in the Oxford Road suffered damage of £1000 .Some parts had a very rare and damaging 4 inches of rain in one hour.

1911: An extraordinary summer with great heat and drought. At Finchampstead, July registered eight days exceeding 90 F (32C) and August, six. A record heat for the county was reached on 9th August at Wokingham when the temperature topped 97.1F (36.1C). There was also a record 842 hours of sun during the three summer months. This year was the warmest recorded for 86 years at Wokingham, while December was extremely wet with over nine inches (230 mm) measured at Farnborough Rectory.

1912: Long Wittenham's weather station began recording in 1851 and for the first time reported a completely dry month in April. August's weather was in complete contrast to that of the previous year. Average temperatures were down ten degrees Fahrenheit and it was variously described as dreadful, wet and cheerless. At Wantage it rained on all but four days.

On 20th November a slight earthquake was felt at 9am in places as far apart as Abingdon and Ascot.

1913: At Abingdon on 29th April 1.78 inches (45 mm) of rain fell in little over an hour causing a flood greater than any other previously experienced within the town.

1914: Sharp frosts on 25th and 26th May did a great deal of damage to crops. A violent storm on 28th December gave truth to the old maxim, "First rise after low foretells an even greater blow". As the barometer rose from 28.60 inches (969 millibars) at Maidenhead, a furious wind blew hard from the northwest turning rain into snow. Many trees were uprooted and parts of the county had 9 inches of rain (230mm) by the end of the month, making it the wettest December in many station records. The Thames Valley was flooded.

1915: Heavy rain in January led to widespread floods with more than six inches of rain in West Berkshire. This was not all good news for the water companies, some of which were literally swamped. The Fobney Works had to resort to more expensive steam pumps while the Kennet and Lodden burst their banks inundating hundreds of homes in the Reading district.

1916: After a benign winter, March brought severe storms on 27th and 28th with tempestuous winds and blinding snow. Tilehurst was completely isolated for several days by fallen trees. Many fine historic trees were blown down and at Sonning 26 huge elms were uprooted in minutes. A description of the area following the storm spoke of the numerous stumps lining the road and how they were pathetic reminders of the ancient elms which at one time beautified the locality and provided cool and grateful shade in the heat of the summer.

1917: During this long cold winter a barge was frozen into the ice at Sonning Bridge. On 4th February six inches of snow fell and the temperature dropped to just 7F (-14C) at Wokingham. A very wet July and August. Reading recorded 5.81 inches (148mm) in July, the wettest since records started in 1879. The mayhem this caused farmers was compounded by a serious lack of labour due to the war.

1918: On 17th January half a foot of snow fell in five hours in Reading and the Thames Valley causing chaos on the tramways. It was a splendid year for crops, especially corn which was felt to be the best ever grown in one season with early dry weather compensated by rains in July.

1919: This year showed a distinct lack of promise as March and April were both wet and cold. There was some snow in March which proved a source of great anxiety to farmers and on Sunday 27th April a violent snowstorm swept the Berkshire Downs. On the Lambourn-Wantage Road, drifts were five to six feet deep. It was a cold year with a chilly autumn.

This picture of Eddington village, near Hungerford could have been taken in September just after the great heat of August 1911.

August 1911 — the hottest ever known

1911 was the year that broke all the records for its great heat. In many parts of the county there were eight days in which the temperature topped 90F in July, and six in August. Day after day the sun beat down relentlessly for more than 10 hours a day and, at Wokingham, on 9th August an all-time record of 97.1F (36.1C) was reached, which lasted until August 1990.

The *North Berks Herald* in its issue of 11th August wrote: "The great heat which prevailed over Berkshire during the third and fourth weeks of July was exceeded on Wednesday by temperatures even more abnormal. On each of the previous occasions the thermometer had risen above 90F in the shade and on 26th July touched 96F. Wednesday's maximum was a degree or two higher — the highest ever recorded in Berkshire, not just for August, but any

summer month".

Sadly, the great heat sent the death rate soaring, particularly in London where 855 children died. In Berkshire two children were drowned, one at Hinksey Ferry and the other in the Cherwell.

In the greatest heat ever known there were many unusual accidents in the county. At Dorchester a horse and wagonette bolted but "was brought under subjection by colliding with a coal cart". In another incident in the village of Benson, "a stranger was passing through the village on a motorbike when he collided with a horse cart, as a result of which he was rendered unconscious."

The organisers of Wallingford Athletics Club's sports day were the most inspired. They cancelled the meeting on August Bank Holiday Monday and substituted it with a "wonderful regatta".

KING'S RAIN...

THUNDER, lightning, deluge and floods. The summer and autumn of 1912 were stormy, wet and cold and the only cheerful sign on the horizon was the impending visit to Hungerford of the newly-crowned King George V, who many thought would bring much-needed sunshine to the county. The big day arrived — Monday 21st October was perfect — and the scene in Hungerford just before the King's arrival was a brilliant one with streets and houses illuminated. Unfortunately, the weather, in true English fashion let everyone down down at the wrong mo-

ment, and the rain cascaded down for most of his visit.. When the King departed on Saturday October 26th crowds of people, wisely carrying umbrellas, were *assembled at the station and the band played enthusiastically but the deepening depression certainly marred the occasion.*

Great wind topples mighty trees

26th-27th March, 1916

A SEVERE gale carrying driving, blinding snow swept across Berkshire on Monday 26th March with a fury that "brought back memories of those great Victorian hurricanes". On the Tuesday, following a dull and quieter morning, the blizzard reasserted itself and grew in violence as the day wore on. All the time the wind whistled, slates were hurled into the streets, walls blown down, mighty trees uprooted and telegraph poles toppled, cutting off communications across the county. "The havoc, wrought by the wind", said the *Berkshire Chronicle*, "presents a melancholy testimony of its overwhelming power. The damage caused in the villages of Pangbourne, Basildon, Goring, Hurst, Twyford, Wargrave, Burghfield, Shurlock Row and Sonning is awesome".

The *Chronicle* continued: "The inhabitants of Tilehurst had a unique experience. The village, lying as it does, very high, caught the full force of the storm and was completely isolated for several days. Trees and telegraph poles were upended and all entrances

blocked with the result that traffic could neither leave nor enter".

One Tilehurst resident had a miraculous escape when a huge elm fell a foot in front of his bicycle, Realising it would be useless to continue his journey he turned back and as he did so another great tree missed him by inches.

Across the county other people were not so lucky. A Basildon villager, named Fuller, was hit by a falling tree and a cyclist in the Datchet Road at Slough had his bike smashed to pieces, Many pedestrians were hurt by falling tiles and wayward branches carried by the wind.

At Windsor, historic trees were blown down in the grounds of the Castle and the forest. The local paper described it as "a perfect blizzard which provided some extraordinary spectacles". There was considerable damage, mainly caused by falling trees, in Slough, Eton, Maidenhead, Wargrave, Shiplake and Reading.

The scene in Northcroft Lane, Newbury after the "disastrous" flooding of 7th January, 1915.

1920 — 1929

Girls on their way to school at Chilton Foliat, just over the Wiltshire border, in July 1923, a notably hot month.

1920: It was a spring-like January with the temperature soaring to 57F (14C) on the 12th in Reading and to 60F (16C) on 17th and 19th February. The winter continued mild. But it was a cool, disappointing summer. It rained on 23 days during July and for the first time the Maidenhead Amateur Regatta had to be postponed owing to the flooded state of the Thames.

1921: An extremely dry year. At Bisham only 12.87 inches (327mm) of rain was recorded, the lowest annual value ever measured in Berkshire. Many square miles of countryside blazed, brooks dried up and there were travel restrictions on the Thames due to the low water levels. On 10th July, 92F (33C) was recorded in Reading, and as late as 6th October the thermometer read 83F (28C).

1922: Summer began early with a heatwave in May. From 21st May to 2nd June the temperature remained above 80F (27C) on ten of the 13 days, reaching 88F (31C) on 22nd. Large crowds of elegantly dressed boating people descended on Maidenhead. July and August, however, were disappointing and it was a wet and disastrous Henley. On 6th July a woman escaped death by seconds during a thunderstorm in Maidenhead. Lightning struck a chimney and the current ran along a washing line where she had just finished hanging out clothes. Her name was Mrs Sparkes.

1923: A wet February with rain on 23 days amounting to 3.74 inches (95.5mm), but the weather improved in March with an early taste of summer on the 29th when 69F (20.6C) was recorded. July was warm with a notable hot spell, the temperature peaking at 95F (35C) on the 12th at Shinfield. A man exposed to the glaring sun whilst on relief work in the Basingstoke Road suddenly collapsed, and later died in hospital. On examination he was found to have reached the extraordinary temperature of 110F (44C). There were several other deaths that afternoon in the Reading district, all attributed to the heatwave.

1924: A wet interval in January caused the River Kennet to flood, producing two feet of water on the Burghfield-Theale road at Burghfield Mill. Nearly two inches of rain fell between the 18th and the 24th, but the weather pendulum swung the other way in February when only 0.36 inches was recorded at Caversham. July was witness to another heatwave with 87F (30.6C) on the 12th. Lord Desburgh in a meeting of the Thames Conservancy in early October stated that rainfall was eight inches above average for the year so far and that at times in September the Thames was flowing at 3,000 million gallons a day. He warned of flooding if rain continued into the winter. It did. Sunninghill finished the year with a precipitation of 38.69 inches (988mm).

1925: The year began with flooding. This was particularly serious at Sonning where the road was four feet under water and a milk-float lived up to its name when it drifted into a ditch. Many miles of countryside were inundated and boards were placed in the streets of Maidenhead so that pedestrians could pass dry-shod. On Sunday, 26th April during an sharp thunderstorm 25 people were rendered homeless when lightning struck a row of houses at Brightwell. The oldest and largest barn in Berkshire, at Hithercroft Farm, Cholsey, was also destroyed.

1926: Once again there was flooding at the start of the year with Wargrave under water and planks placed at Goring. The river at Windsor was three feet, three inches above average. Deep snow fell on 16th January in an otherwise mild month, a foot was measured in Newbury. Several villages, including Faccombe and Ashmansworth, were entirely cut off. Accidents abounded, including a steam wagon which slid out of control down Grove Hill and came crashing through the railings of the lodge entrance to Benham Park, stopping just inches from the building. There were reports of a temperature as low as 0F (- 18C) at Donnington. There was another July heatwave with 88F (31C) on the 14th and an even more remarkable 87F (30.6C) recorded as late as 19th September.

1927: A late surge of warmth on 30th October, with 67F (19.4C) at Reading, punctuated an otherwise wet year. The most memorable weather, however, came in December with an intense freeze that gave rise to perfect skating conditions. One enterprising

From the hill that rises behind the village of Sonning inhabitants have often looked across to the great meander of the River Thames with the flooded plain in the foreground. In the summer of 1921 there were no floods — just days and days of sunshine. This picture, taken in July 1921, shows Sonning in the drought. Even in October temperatures reached the 80's.

young woman set up a brazier on Kingsmere Lake, Wokingham, selling hot drinks to the crowds gathered there. Then came an ice storm on the 21st when it rained for several hours with the mercury well below freezing. A constable, out on his beat, was forced to negotiate the ice-encased Coley Steps on his rear! Reading Hospital was overwhelmed by a spate of broken limbs. Heavy rain on Christmas Day turned to snow and one of the worst blizzards of the twentieth century followed. A considerable stretch of the Reading to Henley Road was under five feet of snow and the railway line from Lambourn to Eastbury was buried under a white mountain 15 feet high. The only way to many villages was on foot across the fields.

1928: After the Christmas snowstorms, early January brought a rapid thaw and vast floods throughout the Thames Valley. There was a striking transformation of weather in March. Sunday 4th was the warmest day on record for so early in the

year at 66F (19C), but Sunday 11th was the coldest in March for 51 years. The thermometer did not rise above freezing and the countryside lay under a mantle of snow. At Sonning the thaw and further rain produced a flood deeper than any since 1894. An immense lake formed and to reach the district a journey had to be made from Caversham. Only the tops of trees could be seen along the river bank. At Newbury, water invaded the station pouring off the Pyle and Wash Hills and covering the tracks with two feet of water.

1929: Rainfall at Upton from the beginning of January to the end of September amounted to only 6.86 inches (175mm), yet from October to the end of the year 15.06 inches (385mm) fell. At Bucklebury a meagre 0.14 inches (3.6mm) was measured during March. February was bitterly cold with the mercury below freezing from the 11th to the 17th both during the day and at night. It was the coldest month since February 1895.

The Boxing Day blizzard

26th December, 1927

PEOPLE woke up on Christmas morning 1927 to drenching rain. The muddy landscape on that dull, dreary and almost mild morning was a far cry from the snow scenes on Christmas cards. By nightfall, all had changed. The heavy rain had turned first to sleet, then thick, wet snow. A few hours later a fully fledged blizzard had blown up and the temperature had plunged to freezing point.

Guests who had arrived in the downpour were barely able to get home as the blinding snow swept down late in the evening, settling readily and blowing around in the strong winds. By Boxing Day morning there were drifts so deep that scores of Berkshire roads were impassable and some villages were marooned for days. Many events, sporting and otherwise, had to be cancelled. These included the annual Wallingford Cottage Hospital ball.

The road from Theale to Pangbourne after the Boxing Day blizzard in December 1927

The Reading-Mortimer-Tadley route was badly affected and although Mortimer could be reached, the drifts were ten feet deep beyond this area. For three days omnibuses were unable to get to Wantage over the Berkshire Downs. An enterprising farmer on the Wallingford to Oxford road charged two shillings to drag motor cars across his fields to by-pass obstructing drifts on the main road at Dorchester. Near Newbury, the snow was up to five feet high where it had drifted on Greenham Hill. Gangs of villagers came out with shovels and spades to cut a path through.

Roads in and around Henley were blocked but it did not stop some 250 people from attending a dance at the Town Hall on Boxing night. The town's cinema was also well patronised. During the storm, the houseboat 'Merrythought' broke loose but was fortunately captured and re-fastened before any significant damage occurred. The village of Harwell, south of Didcot, was cut off as a result of huge snow drifts at Blenheim Hill. One drift was 100 yards long and almost six feet deep. Clearance teams worked long hours and bus services were eventually resumed on December 27th. The road to Newbury from Rowstock Corner was still piled high with drifts some days later and was impassable to motor vehicles for the best part of a week.

During the week that followed, communities worked long hours to clear the frost-hardened snow from roads and paths; later nature took over and the piles of snow quickly thawed causing flooding.

On the Reading to Henley road there were tremendous drifts. Motor cars were abandoned in some which were five feet deep. Between Maidenhead and Slough, conditions were similar. Those living in the Sheffield Bottom and Pinge Wood districts of Burghfield had to struggle against snow that was waist deep. Numerous telephone and telegraph wires were brought down across the county; 500 of them in the Reading district alone.

The great snowstorm was caused when an area of low pressure from the Atlantic Ocean moved from Ireland to the English Channel.. Winds backed to the east bringing very cold air from the continent trurning the rain to snow. Further west of Berkshire there were even worse conditions and on Salisbury Plain, the drifts were as high as 20 feet.

Many tobogganers took to the slopes of Prospect Park, Reading, Caversham Heights and Pangbourne Hill to enjoy the freezing conditions. The *Berkshire Chronicle* reported that there were many 'old world' scenes. But the delirium on the downs was soon replaced by despair downstream when the Thames and other rivers overflowed as the snow melted.

It was necessary to be well protected from the icy elements when venturing forth in late December 1927; this was the scene on the Wallingford to Henley Road.

Cemetery Junction, Reading after the great Boxing Day snowstorm.

The wild waters of the Kennet

lst — 6th January, 1928

THE great Christmas snowstorm of 1927 was followed in January by the great deluge, the great thaw and then, inevitably, the greatest flooding since 1894. It was on New Year's Day, after another blizzard, that the rain poured down from a leaden sky, accompanied by much warmer weather. The snow thawed rapidly, the Thames burst its banks and hundreds of thousands of gallons of fast-flowing flood water raced across the lush valleys into towns, villages and hamlets. Adjacent rivers could not cope with the sheer weight and speed of the water. Flood defences, such as they were, capitulated and vast lakes were created right across Berkshire. People were trapped in upstairs rooms, trees and shrubs were torn from the ground, bridges collapsed, supplies were cut off and sewage spewed from blocked drains to form a sea of sludge. By Wednesday 4th January at Caversham Weir, the river had risen 23 inches over the normal summer level — a rise of 15 inches in 24 hours. In London, also, it was still rising, but there was worse to come.

During the night of 6th-7th January a storm in the North Sea caused a tidal surge. The Thames was already swollen. Now it was raised to its highest-recorded level and disaster was almost inevitable. In London, 14 people, including four young sisters, were drowned. The vaults of the Palace of Westminster were flooded, the normally dry moat of the Tower of London was filled to capacity and valuable paintings in the Tate Gallery were badly damaged.

Meanwhile, in Berkshire, vast volumes of water were now being emptied into the Thames from its many tributaries. The Kennet, transformed into a wild, destructive, fast-flowing sea of mud, attracted record crowds of people to Reading to watch the extraordinary flow of the river as it passed under, and eventually over, Blake's Bridge. By now motorists were coming to grief, men were being taken to work in farm waggons and housewives had to be sent out in boats to obtain the day's supplies.

On the Arborfield Road, the licensee of the Magpie and Parrot woke up to find water two feet deep on the floor of his bar. The towpath along the Kennet had disappeared, timber yards and wharfs were inundated and residents in nearby houses had quickly moved all vital possessions and themselves into upstairs rooms.

The *Berkshire Chronicle* reported on Friday 6th January that the river levels were still rising. "Those who were brave or foolish enough to stand on Sonning Bridge on Thursday found themselves in the middle of a vast lake — the low-lying land being submerged for miles. The Henley road to Sonning is impassable. Boathouses and riverside bungalows are totally submerged. Of the trees on the river bank, only the tops are visible."

At Maidenhead, the sluices were opened and the water began to find its way to Bridge Road, flooding all the intervening land. The *Advertiser* said: "The lower part of Maidenhead is a veritable Venice and there is punting on the main road." A flood committee was formed to visit in parties the areas where people needed help to get to and from their homes.

At Newbury, the flood covered the railway tracks and was pouring into the railway station. In the town, thanks to the precautionary methods of raising all the hatches, the floods were kept to a minimum but the canal had overflowed its banks and the sluices at West Mills were raised to their fullest extent, relieving the pressure of the water in the canal and diverting a large volume into the stream at Northcroft. Below the town, the valley of the Kennet was under water. At Thatcham, the roads became rivers.

The *Berkshire Chronicle* said the stream which presented the most remarkable picture of all was the Enborne. "Normally this is a small winding stream which rises under the Hampshire hills at West Woodhay and discharges into the Kennet at Padworth. On Monday afternoon (2nd January) it assumed the proportions of a mighty rushing river, flowing 100 yards wide and several feet above the road level. At Newtown Water it encircled the Swan Inn, routing out a party who were having lunch and driving the landlord and his wife to upstairs rooms. He did not go, however, until he had lashed the beer barrels in the cellar to their supports and lifted the piano onto the parlour table."

At 12 feet above its normal level, the Enborne made an impassable barrier between the two counties at Aldern Bridge, Bishop's Green Ford and Thornford Bottom. Every neighbouring hamlet and village was flooded, including Brimpton, Wasing, Aldermaston, Kingsclere and Donnington.

THE FLOODS near READING BRIDGE.

January, 1928.

January, 1928. Punting for a pint at the Reform public house, Maidenhead, suitably situated next to St. Mary's Mission Hall.

Skating at Whiteknights Park, Reading in February, 1929.

The coldest since 1895

February 1929 was the coldest February in Berkshire since 1895 and destined to remain one of the coldest of the twentieth century. For six days between the 11th and 17th, the temperature remained below freezing both day and night as an enormous anticyclone over northeast Europe drove bitterly cold air across the county.

The Thames was frozen from bank to bank, as were all the rivers in Berkshire. Skating, the great winter sport for all ages, took place on every river, lake and pond and there were many casualties. It was not a good month for old people. Many perished from the effects of hypothermia and several others died after falls; in fact the Reading Coroner, Mr J.L. Martin, held three inquests on one day on aged people who died after falling on the ice.

Floods in Charnham Street, Hungerford on May 16th, 1932

1930 — 1939

The river bank at Wallingford in August 1932 — a month in which the temperature reached well into the nineties.

1930: Winds gusted over 60mph during a severe gale on the evening of 12th January. Virtually all the roads leading from Maidenhead were blocked by fallen trees and the railway line north from the town to High Wycombe similarly succumbed, cutting telegraphic links as well.

1931: In a snowstorm on Tuesday, 10th March, a fireman was thrown from his appliance as it was being driven to an emergency at Cold Ash. He rolled over several times, knocked his head on the kerbstone and dented his helmet but otherwise escaped with just a few bruises. The temperature fell to 20F (-6.7C) on the 10th but a week later the mercury reached 63F (17C), encouraging picnickers onto the Downs at Cholsey.

1932: A hot year with many thunderstorms. Hungerford was flooded on May 16th. A remarkable heatwave produced an afternoon temperature of 96F (35.6C) on 19th August. There were a number of drowning accidents including one man who died after plunging into Hurley Pool. In the *Reading Mercury* there was an unusual picture of Brigadier General J. Wroughton in shorts and vest tending his garden with an electric fan heater rigged up to keep him cool. Charles II wrote: "The English summer comprises of three fine days and a thunderstorm", and this year it came true. A tumultuous storm swept Berkshire during the evening of 20th August. More than two inches of rain fell and at Crowthorne, the roof of the Wesleyan Church was damaged and houses struck during a spectacular lightning display.

1933: In what was to prove a very dry year, the Marlow Regatta and many other fetes and shows were, nevertheless, marred by rain on 24th June. Two days later a Hungerford man was killed when his house was struck by lightning. His hand had been close to a radio receiver with an outside aerial. A friend who was with him in the house said that suddenly a red ball of fire burst into the room. The weather relented and the Henley Regatta a week later had a splendid atmosphere with 91F (33C) on 3rd July. The dry, hot conditions continued almost unabated until the middle of September. In August almost half the days brought temperatures in excess of 80F, with the Bank Holiday soaring to 93F (34C) as thousands fled to the coast by train. However the heat brought its problems in a series of major heathland fires, dwindling water supplies and a spate of drownings in the county's rivers and lakes. December was very cold with frost on as many as 25 nights.

1934: An unusually dry winter with only two inches (53.8mm) of rain at Wokingham. Dense fog prevailed at times in January and on the 24th, visibility was down to three yards in places accompanied by a frost. The AA was swamped with calls from people who had abandoned their cars and patrols acted as pilots through the murk. Fog flares were in operation at Twyford, Maidenhead, Denham, Langley and Henley. Ironically, there was also a severe gale in January which blew with such force that Howberry Park, the Wallingford home of Lady Wittenham, was badly damaged when a large chestnut tree collapsed on to it. A bedroom was almost demolished. There was also considerable chaos in Lambourn where the windows of many houses were shattered by the wind's velocity. With south-westerly winds prevailing, December was so mild that many places escaped a frost. What a contrast to the year before!

1935: A sudden thunderstorm on 11th July took hundreds of Thames bathers by surprise and onlookers became as wet as the swimmers. During the squall the wind drove the rain with such force that many buildings needed repointing, so much mortar having been loosened. There was a fine August Bank Holiday with the mercury at 80F (27C) and record traffic on the Thames led to talk of "the good old days on the river". The dry August weather, however, gave rise to a poor cereal harvest. On the night of Monday 16th, one of the wildest September gales ever recorded swept over England and continued with unabated violence into the following day. It caused death and destruction.

Break time for 15 harvesters in a Thames Valley field. This picture was taken in the mid-30s when there were many splendid summers. As the horses are all wearing shaft harnesses it is clear the carting had started. The young man with the gun is probably the farmer's son.

1936: After a thaw of snow which had fallen the previous month, and heavy rain in the early part of January, the familiar flood story unfolded. At Windsor ferry the river was almost a mile wide and a rower was tragically drowned in the turbulent waters after his boat was swamped during a practice for the Reading University maiden eights. It was a wintry Easter and people sought refuge in cinemas and theatres. A furious snowstorm during the evening of Bank Holiday Monday, 12th April, piled up snow almost six inches deep in just over an hour.

1937: March was the coldest month of the winter and 2,000 subscribers in the Reading district alone lost their telephone lines during the weekend of 6th March when a thick and wet snowstorm swept the county. Further rain and a thaw caused the village of Bucklebury to be flooded by the River Pang. Many houses and the post office were marooned.

1938: Spring was extremely dry and by June appeals went out for an urgent saving of water as the average daily consumption reached five million gallons in the Reading area. The August Bank Holiday was splendid and 88F (31C) was recorded on 1st August. Even as late as 5th November the mercury still attained an almost summer-like warmth of 68F (20C). In December a biting east wind set in on the

17th. With a temperature of only 23F (-5C) many pipes froze. One Caversham plumber was so busy attending to others that his own house suffered a burst. Demand for paraffin at one shop reached 200 gallons a day. Twelve inches of snow cut off Newbury from the outside world but one postman was not to be beaten. Despite having to be dug out from beneath six feet of snow at Combe, he continued in his van until he slid down a hill and hit a tree, which was fortunately placed as it saved him from a 200 foot drop! He then abandoned his van in a barn and delivered mail on foot, with the snow up to his chest in places. Were it not for his 17 stone he would have probably succumbed to the cold but he succeeded in reaching Combe Post Office, exhausted but still defiant. Together with two engineers, he dug a 500 yard track through the snow to extricate his van. Snow continued to fall up to Boxing Day.

1939: In what was generally a mild January, a sudden moist and sticky snowstorm brought havoc on the 25th. More than 7,000 subscribers lost telephone lines in Reading and it was impossible to run buses between Mortimer and Tadley. At Bradfield a large garage collapsed under the sheer weight of snow and many of the county's public clocks stopped due to the encumbrance of a thick and icy mantle.

The burning summer of 1933

THE summer of 1933 was glorious. During July, August and September the sun bore down onto a parched earth and Berkshire, like much of England, wilted in the heat as every day seemed to be hotter than the last. Food had to be thrown away, cattle died for want of water, people struggled to keep cool and as the county became tinder dry the threat of fires became very real.

The villagers of Bradfield faced the threats with a calm assurance, for a gleaming red fire engine was on standby — ready to deal with any blazing problem that the burning sun might offer. When Mr Wilson's barn went up the inhabitants realised they were in a quandary. The village had no brigade and no-one knew how to drive the engine. Undeterred, they formed a fire-fighting chain, handing buckets of water down the line. The barn was saved and so too was Mr Wilson's house.

Other Berkshire villages, amply supplied with fire hydrants, found they hadn't any water. In Bucklebury, during the worst of the 1933 drought, the village wells were completely dry.

A similar problem faced the people of Wokingham. When a large woodland area at Sandhurst went up in flames early in September, the town fire crew adopted the primitive method of beating it out. The job took hours, only to be followed by the largest heath fire ever known in Berkshire. The blaze began on the Blackwater side of the Hartford Bridge flats and advanced rapidly, gorging itself on heather, trees and shrubs covering five miles in eight hours.

This time troops from Aldershot came to the rescue.

Bathers on the river bank at Wallingford in the summer of 1933.

A few of those glorious days

There were five days in June when the temperature exceeded 80 F (27C) followed by 14 days in July. August began with more sunshine and the following readings:

2nd August: 85F
3rd August: 84F
4th August: 86F
5th August: 88F
6th August: 93F
7th August: 87F
8th August: 83F
9th August: 82F

There were six further days in the month when the temperature climbed into the eighties.

Elephants pick up fallen trees

17th September, 1935

THIS was a most violently destructive storm. With winds gusting in excess of 100 miles-an-hour, it arrived in Berkshire on the back of a deep depression which had moved swiftly across Ireland and during the night of Monday 16th and the morning of Tuesday 17th September, 1935 it created mayhem. It rearranged the countryside, sucked roofs and walls from houses, plunged homes into darkness, pulled down miles of telephone wires and then left, almost as suddenly as it had arrived.

Accompanied by torrential rain the gale swept in at 10 pm on Monday and raged all night. Few slept. As trees began to fall, corporation workmen from Reading, Maidenhead, Windsor, Newbury and Hungerford were called from their beds to help clear the roads of debris. Every AA patrol in the county battled with fallen trees entangled with the remains of telephone wires It was a dangerous and difficult task.

The hat, dress and boots look as if they come from another era — and they probably do — but this picture of an old lady and her yoke was taken in the summer of 1933 when the wells almost dried up and fetching water was a serious business. With a determination which was such a feature of country life in those days, the lady makes her way along a lane in Twyford.

Many escaped serious injury but one man from Amity Road, Reading was killed on Tuesday morning, buried under a fall of clay at the Binfield Brick and Tile Works. A cook, living in the servants' quarters at Broomhall, Sunningdale, had a miraculous escape when a tree crashed through the roof and came to rest four feet from her bed. Next door, in the parlourmaid's room, part of the ceiling fell down. A woman from Hungerford, hurrying home on Monday night after a carnival dance, was struck by a galvanised piece of iron. She was bowled over by the blow but lived to tell the tale.

At Hartford Bridge Flats, near Blackwater, a saloon car was blown off the road and at Owlsmoor, Sandhurst a wooden bungalow was picked up by the wind and dumped into the garden next door. In each case the owners survived. At Medmenham, so many trees crashed that elephants from a travelling circus were employed to pick them from the road. A cricket pavilion at Hartley Wespall was wrecked and at Thatcham, hotel signs, tobacco advertisements, bricks, tiles and trees were strewn all over the High Street. The roof was blown off the hangar at Woodley Aerodrome and many machines were damaged.

There was chaos all over Berkshire. Roads and railway lines were blocked by fallen trees, electricity failed in most areas, hundreds of chimney pots tumbled and windows were blown in. At Windsor, river craft were torn from their moorings and blown downstream. It was the same story at Henley, Wantage was totally isolated and at Maidenhead it looked as if a bomb had exploded in the town centre.

For several hours life came to a standstill. But Berkshire picked itself up and, thanks to the stalwart work of the services, normality was resumed. It was certainly a storm to remember.

Two men pitching wheat sheaves on to the harvest wagon and a third loading. This scene of high summer on an estate in the Thames Valley was taken in the late 1930s when the sun shone brightly.

Several dry summers and a rainless spring had resurrected fears that the climate was changing and water was going to be at a premium in future years. In fact, an expert in geology at Reading University, Professor H.Hawkins told Rotarians on 19th September, 1935 that the Reading area was the driest place in the British Isles by a long way and it was wrong to believe that the east coast was. "Practically every fine evening this summer I have been out onto the Berkshire Downs looking for water in an attempt to satisfy the requirements of some rural council or other. I have failed. All the water which fell on or found its way on to the Downs was mopped up by the vast chalk sponge while the clay prevented it from sinking fully."

He said that all the springs that issue into the Vale of the White Horse had failed and wells which used to be 250 feet deep now needed to be 500 feet deep in some parts to reach water "On average the water level would seem to have shrunk about 175 feet.

"Recently, through the drought, the upper course of the Pang had been grassgrown, the Lambourn was a good deal short of its usual length and the Kennet had been about 20 miles short. These periods of falling levels had occurred before", he said. "In the Bronze Age the Downs people did not have to go far for deep water and in Roman times, water could be obtained 200 feet above the present day levels. The Berkshire Downs, which used to be a centre of civilisation is now practically a wilderness. They are steadily draining".

1st August, 1938 was Bank Holiday Monday and the temperature in Berkshire had climbed to the upper eighties Fahrenheit. No wonder the river bank at Windsor was so popular — but then it was the same story all the way down the Thames.

1940 — 1949

A lucky escape for this driver on Kennet Side, Reading in January 1947.

1940: A bitterly cold January with an average temperature at Reading of just 30.4F (-0.9C). The first bitter winter of the war. See P.63

1941: A snowy winter, a cold May and a wet August.

1942: The third consecutive snowy winter with snow recorded on at least 35 days during January and February.

1943: Winds from the Atlantic produced a very unsettled January and a particularly savage gale on the night of the 30th when the wind speed exceeded 70mph. One farmhouse near Henley had the entire roof of its western wing, some 120 feet long, 24 feet wide and 23 feet high, lifted from its wall plates and flung to the ground in a mass of twisted timbers. Meanwhile torrential rain flooded Maidenhead and residents of Bray and Cookham awoke to find themselves marooned.

1944: Berkshire fruit growers, in common with those in other parts of the country, suffered badly due to late spring frosts. In some areas farmers lost fortunes in a few hours. Lack of rain during the spring months was to blame. The clear skies meant greater losses of heat from the dry soil through night time radiation. Whitsun and August Bank Holiday were excellent weather-wise, the latter encouraging brisk business on the river.

1945: A January remarkable for its diversity with intense cold, snow, icy gales and dense fog. At Caversham a sheet of ice formed on the river from bank to bank and the upper reaches of the Lodden and Kennet were frozen sufficiently to walk across.

Temperatures fell as low as 12F (-11C) on many mornings. Milk was frozen in the churn and there were snowdrifts four feet deep on the Berkshire Downs between Wantage and Streatley. What a transformation then, in February which turned out to be a very mild month having temperatures as high as 61F (16C).

1946: Snow bedecked the countryside briefly on the weekend of 19th and 20th January and ice was thick enough for skating on Kingsmere, Crowthorne. Heavy rains in July and August led to a disastrous harvest. Twenty-five per cent of the wheat was useless and a total of 50% of the crops were damaged. At least the weather relented for the first post-war Bank Holiday and happy, laughing crowds were found everywhere basking in the sun. The rains began again in November and there was widespread flooding. A double decker bus was ditched in deep water at Cookham and some of the passengers "got a little wet" before they were rescued by boat.

1947: The winter remembered most by those born before 1943, followed by the infamous floods. (See pages 67-78.)A warm summer followed, the average maximum for August being 80.9F (27.2C) at Shinfield near Reading. During a thunderstorm in August a sizzling fire ball struck a house at Blewbury, Didcot, shot out of a window and knocked a branch off a tree.

1948: Shinfield reached 92F (33C) on 30th July and Wokingham peaked at 93F (34C) on 29th July but the Bank Holiday was disappointing;ten thousand people were soaked at a fete at Hills Meadow, Reading. More than half an inch fell in a very short space of time. One of the worst fogs of the century descended on the Thames Valley towards the end of November. For seven days a thick, clinging blanket dampened streets, deterred shoppers and slowed traffic to a walking pace. Drivers were warned not to travel and many of those who did lost their way.

1949: Kingsmere Lake had dried up by early July and the warm, dry summer continued throughout September. It was one of the best corn harvests for years. Demand for water was eight per cent higher than the previous year with a peak daily consumption of 6,332 million gallons in June.

Mrs. Ethel Philbrick of Cold Ash, near Newbury took these fascinating pictures of glaze, a rare meteorological phenomenon. The weight of the glaze, caused by rain at a freezing temperature, solidifying into ice as it landed, caused many tree branches to bend and break. This occurred on 27th January, 1940, continuing through 28th and 29th January across a large area of southern England, and was one of the most famous such "ice storms" ever. Falling boughs of beech trees encased in ice could be heard crashing down making a quite terrifying noise on the night of the 28th/29th. In the daytime it became almost impossible to stand upright on sloping road surfaces; leaves on shrubs rattled in the wind and many birds died in flight.

Windsor swans encased in ice

Winter of 1940

THE winter of 1940 was one of the coldest of the century. It was also a secret. While Berkshire was paralysed by some of the bleakest conditions since 1895, the news was being suppressed for fear it would be of use to the enemy.

The freezing weather set in during the last days of December 1939 but it was early February before the full story could be told of one of the most severe frosts on record. On 3rd February, 1940, the *Reading Mercury* broke the silence with typical British understatement. "It is now possible to reveal", it said, "that it was very cold indeed early in January."

In fact the weather had been so bitter that the Thames had frozen over — the first time this had been seen since the Wallingford freeze of 1929. At Reading, the *Mercury* reported, the ice extended from the 'danger' post near Reading Lock to De Montfort Island and at Windsor, day-trippers arrived by their hundreds to experience the first freeze of the river at this spot since an ox was roasted on it in 1895.

Such conditions provided wonderful entertainment for those brave enough to don skates. Windsor Great Park, Windsor Great Forest and Whiteknights lake in Reading were packed with people making the most of the ice. Animals were less fortunate, however. At Windsor some of the swans were rescued, having become encased in ice. They were sent to the "swan's hospital" suffering from exposure! An Alsatian dog and a swan were also found frozen in Whiteknights lake. The dog had been missing for some time and it was assumed the swan had been a victim of its long and desperate search for food.

Although the harsh weather claimed no human casualties it brought it's share of distress and hardship. Some families in King's Road, Reading survived nearly two weeks without water while in other parts of the town homes were flooded. Plumbers worked around the clock to fix burst water pipes. One house at Caversham was completely awash from a burst water tank and at Emmer Green water poured from a pipe for three days before the family returned from a trip visiting relatives.

A shortage of fuel led to the closure of many schools and delivery men, already impeded by the blackout, struggled against the odds to perform their public duties. One Reading laundry van driver spent a night in his vehicle after becoming stuck in the snow in the unfortunately named Deadman's Lane near Goring Heath. Bus drivers, too, suffered similar experiences as they were stranded in remote parts of the countryside. In fact there was delay and confusion all round as trains failed to materialise, cars were abandoned and queues formed in the "biggest traffic hold up this country has ever known".

The *North Berks Herald* said that plumbers were receiving calls every hour of the day and one of them had no fewer than 300 entered on his books in the course of two days. In Didcot and Abingdon it was so cold that housewives had considerable difficulty in getting frozen milk out of the bottles while those cyclists who braved the conditions almost qualified as circus riders.

"Not for many years", reported the *Herald*, "has there been such a demand for heating appliances to thaw out pipes and those few who came out of the ordeal without any burst pipes must feel particularly grateful."

In Cold Ash, Newbury, and many other places in southern England, rain fell while the temperature was below freezing and as the rain hit the ground it covered everything with a varnish-like glaze. Telegraph wires were weighed down and many poles sagged.

Fun on the frozen river, as seen from Caversham bridge, Reading in 1940.

Snow-covered roofs as seen from the tower of St Laurence's Church, Reading on Saturday morning 12th January 1947. Traffic was moving at a snail's pace through the Market Square.

The winter of discontent

January — March, 1947

FOR those who lived through it, 1947 was the year of meteorological extravaganza. Its very mention conjures up in senior citizens mental pictures of snowdrifts, disastrous floods and, just when it was needed most, a gloriously hot summer.

Coming so soon after the war, the great freeze-up which commenced at the end of January and went on for some seven weeks was ill-timed. It brought seemingly endless misery to thousands of people.As persistent easterly winds brought day after day of bleak skies and snow, families suffered greatly when coal supplies couldn't get through because of drifts. Factories were forced to lay off their workforces and power cuts became widespread. Near Newbury, the temperature plunged to just -1F(-18C). Then, when the thaw did arrive in mid-March, tremendous floods swamped the county and a ferocious gale wrought havoc.

The flooding in Windsor, Eton and Datchet was so severe, it was ranked as one of the district's worst natural disasters. Thousands of homes were submerged and hundreds of families were evacuated. It took months, not weeks, to clear up and in the years that followed, very costly flood defence schemes were constructed to prevent a repeat of the catastrophe. Here is a diary of that dreaded winter, caused by persistent high pressure over the Continent feeding in bitterly cold air and grey, leaden skies.

31st January: Daily power cuts were widespread after the electricity board was forced to save fuel. Aldermaston Airfield was closed owing to a lack of coal. Deliveries of coal to many places were severely hampered by snow and ice.

2nd February: The first Sunday power cut as the coal crisis worsened.

5th February: The road between Wantage and Lambourne was blocked by an expanse of snow four feet deep with drifts up to 12 feet.

6th February: Lambourn was almost isolated, accessible only from Newbury. Only daily work of a snow-plough kept the road open.

7th February: Hardly any potatoes were available in shops. Mr Shinwell, Minister of Fuel and Power, announced in the House of Commons that widespread electricity cuts would be increased owing to the deteriorating coal situation. Three thousand employees of Miles Aircraft were laid off and 80 per cent of Reading's Huntley and Palmer workforce.

8th February: A heavy fall of snow at night after a week of frost and east winds. It was the deepest snow cover of the winter. Snow-ploughs were out for the first time in some rural areas. Miles Aircraft staff in Reading agreed to work one day a week without heat. Brewers, H & G Simonds were only able to produce half their normal output and were working "hand to mouth" with available coal. Reading Gas Company was obliged to reduce pressure. Conditions on the Berkshire Downs were the most severe since 1940. Outlying farmsteads were marooned by snow. There were drifts up to 12 feet deep on the Wantage Road at Eastbury. Newbury shops sold out of paraffin and stoves.

9th February: A very wintry Sunday. Reading Corporation sent out loudspeaker vans calling for their own staff to report for work to clear roads of snow.

12th February: Reading had a maximum temperature of only 28F(-2C) after an overnight low of just 9F(-13C).

15th February: Many Berkshire firms closed and the situation looked very grim with a bleak outlook for factories. Mass unemployment was predicted.Domestic users flouting the switch-off law faced a £100 fine or three months' imprisonment. There was a huge demand for torches, candles, oil lamps and stoves, hurricane lamps, paraffin oil and wicks.

25th February: The sun came out after three weeks but the clear skies led to intense frosts at night. A remarkably low temperature of -3F(-19C) was measured at Abingdon.

1st and 2nd March: A weekend of brilliant sunshine when, for the first time in weeks, the temperature rose above 40F(4C). However, the nights remained exceptionally cold with 14F(-10C) recorded at Reading.

4th March: Hopes of a thaw were dashed when a memorable blizzard dislocated transport across the county. Snow lay up to ten inches deep in north Berkshire.

5th March: Rain fell and froze as it hit sub-zero surfaces. Trees, fences and roads were coated with clear ice. The temperature stayed close to freezing all day and that night more snow fell, which froze hard. Train services were thrown into chaos. The thaw was no longer expected to reach Berkshire — the warmer air staying further south. Many villages around Newbury were cut off. Milk-lorry drivers spent hours digging their way out of farms. Ten foot drifts were reported; the worst snows "in memory" at Hungerford. 200 miles of roads were impassable. No major routes were open at all. Fawley village and Combe were isolated for four days.

7th March: Night-time temperatures at Mapledurham were down to 15F(-9C). A milk quota was introduced at Reading owing to difficulties of getting supplies through.

10th March: Many trains on the Great Western Railway faced long delays owing to thick, night-time fog in Newbury and Reading.

14th March: Serious flooding as the snow melted. The rivers Thames, Kennet and Loddon burst their banks. Riverside dwellers moved belongings to top

Ice Hockey on the lake in Kingsmere Park, Reading in February 1947.

floors. At Fobney pumping station, the water was within four inches of the record high level in 1894. Water was rising three inches in as many hours. At Kentwood Hill, Tilehurst, lower rooms of seven houses were under almost three feet of water. One woman climbed out of a window and along a garden fence to raise the alarm. Neighbours took groceries, bread and milk up a ladder to one family. Customers of the Bull and Chequers public house in Woodley had to walk the plank to patronise the tavern. On the Purley estate, bungalow dwellers had to abandon their homes. The water at Pangbourne Station almost covered the rails as it flowed along the tracks and on to a main road.

15th March: A rapid thaw led to disastrous flooding. 1,600 homes in Caversham were under water, with some ground floors under several feet. Hundreds of families were forced to live in upstairs rooms. The river at Caversham was four feet above normal and only six inches beneath the record-breaking level in 1894. All drinking water had to be boiled before consuming, householders were told in broadcasts. Despite pleas for a drop in consumption, demand for water increased. Floods swamped pumping plants and turbines failed.

16th March: A Sunday storm caused great damage, adding to the misery of Berkshire families. The south-westerly gale, with gusts reaching around 80mph, was blamed for two deaths in Reading. A

young man and woman were injured in St Laurence's churchyard in Reading when masonry crashed down in the storm. The woman, from Woodley, suffered the severance of a big toe, when her foot was crushed. Her male friend from Sandhurst's military establishment also had a foot crushed. In Camberley, on the Berkshire/Surrey border, a woman was killed. At Sonning, a shed roof was blown 100 yards on to the roof of a house. Innumerable trees were uprooted.

18th-25th March: Two hundred aged, sick and infirm people were evacuated from their homes with the help of police using boats and large lorries. Many were taken to makeshift accommodation at Battle Hospital. People in the flooded areas were given tickets for hot food to be used at nearby civic restaurants. Reading Women's Voluntary Service toured the area supplying hot food and drinks. Loud hailer announcements in Caversham warned householders not to tip lavatory water in the floods because of the great health risk. Horses and vans were used to get milk and bread supplies to stricken districts. In some cases, postmen in punts used long poles to hand mail to flood victims in upstairs rooms. Most schools shut around Caversham. Hundreds of phones were out of order. The Mayor of Reading opened a flood relief fund. A further spell of rain with a third of an inch on 19th March, exacerbated the situation.

In Windsor, the Red Cross handed out mattresses,

Undeterred, the bus splashed on, through Bray, towards Maidenhead.

blankets and pillows to people forced to leave their homes. Around 1,350 homes in 25 Windsor streets were flooded. An estimated 6,100 people were affected — almost a third of the town's population.

At Maidenhead, the River Thames was nearly a mile wide. Thousands were evacuated. The Army, together with police and council staff, joined up to help with the flood operations. The railway line between Bourne End and Maidenhead was impassable. Damage at Windsor was more serious than in 1894. Windsor Gas Works was put out of action and supplies diverted from Slough after assistance was procured from a diver. The military built a dam to prevent an inundation of Windsor's water works.

The rise of water in the Thames at Windsor was over eight feet. The Southern Railway track between Windsor and Datchet was unable to take trains; water seeped through to the Clewer end of town and engulfed the racecourse, the Maidenhead Road and Duley's Field, reaching Clarence Road. It was one of the town's worst natural disasters. Army amphibious vehicles were brought in from Aldershot to assist in evacuations. The whole of the lower part of Windsor was under three to four feet of water. Half the patients in Windsor Hospital were evacuated.

At Wraysbury, a lorryload of women being moved to safety ran into trouble and became very agitated. A Sergeant Murname, who was the driver, became a remarkable hero in a bizarre sequence of events. He swam 200 yards to a telephone, only to find it was cut off. He then located a radio ham who put out an SOS message which was picked up in Milan, Italy, by an Englishman. The receiver then sent the message back to Heston, Middlesex, where another ham rang Scotland Yard, who in turn informed Slough Police, who went to the aid of the lorry.

Vast areas of Eton and Datchet were submerged. The Bridge House Hotel at Eton had water pouring through the building, but staff and residents voted to stay put. The riverside doors of the restaurant were swept away by the force of the water and tables, chairs and a piano all vanished to be smashed to pieces over the weir. Wraysbury hardly had a building not surrounded by water. The King and Queen sent a message of sympathy to the inhabitants of the Thames Valley. Hundreds of sightseers swarmed into the stricken areas to witness the spectacle. At Eton, the flood level was only half an inch below the 1894 level — at Egham it was matched.

A rescue party set out in the raging torrents to save some broody hens near Eton College. Their punt nearly sank in the operation and some hens were drowned in the process. Among those saved was "an extremely talkative" cock. Twenty small pigs and two dozen fowls were drowned when piggeries were flooded at East Garston near Newbury, where the Lambourn river overflowed into several low-lying

A Thames Valley businessman took his water taxi home to Maidenhead, 19th March,1947.

areas, flooding homes and pubs, including the Dog Inn. The landlord of the Three Horseshoes Inn at Donnington village lost 44 chicken. Many families suffered flooding at Chilton Foliat where a two-mile stretch of the Kennet had overflowed.

There were some lighter moments in the otherwise tragic month. An Eton College master who was a former Cambridge rowing Blue, accepted a challenge to shoot Windsor Weir in a canoe. This dangerous sport was a favourite pastime with young Guards officers stationed in Windsor prior to 1914. To attempt the feat with the Thames a raging torrent was very

risky indeed. However, the Etonian not only cleared the weir brilliantly but went on to shoot the Black Potts "rapids" and finally reached dry land in the grounds of Windsor Castle near Frogmore House.

At Maidenhead, the daughter of a well-known tradesman swam down the lower end of the High Street for a wager and received a loud cheer from the spectators. With no other sport able to be embarked upon, boat races in Windsor's streets became a popular activity. One man for a bet took a skiff around Eton, stopping at ten pubs on the way and downing a pint at each one!

The amphibious taxi service also ferried people to and from their flooded homes in Windsor, 17th March 1947.

This was Great Knollys Street, Reading in March 1947

Rowing home with the supplies to Washington Road, Caversham.

An armoured vehicle on another rescue mission, on 12th March at Bray; rivers were rising everywhere as the snow thawed.

Thames Valley Police put their emergency plan into action and divided the county into three sections. Here, a constable used a telephone box as his "headquarters" to receive calls from besieged families.

The Maidenhead punts were put to good use. Here, a few of the town's businessmen and women were taken to dry land.

Time to "wet the whistle". Relief workers took a break in a flooded saloon at Wraysbury.

An army DUKW tows a broken-down lorry in the floods at Windsor.

Shopping in Maidenhead town centre by rubber dinghy.

The village of Datchet in the great floods of 1947.

Not a good day for banking or phoning a friend at Datchet.

Buses lost in great 'peasouper'

25th November — 1st December 1948

THE fog which descended on the Thames Valley during the last week of November, 1948 was one of the worst of the twentieth century — so dense, in fact, that movement, even on foot in familiar places, was impossible.

This was a radiation fog, a phenomenon of river valleys and low lying areas most frequent during the long nights of early winter. It formed in Berkshire on Thursday 25th November and, for seven days, Thameside towns and villages lay completely hidden in one of the heaviest blankets ever known. In these conditions shoppers stayed at home, traffic on main roads was reduced to chaos, buses got lost in country lanes, trains were cancelled, sports matches abandoned and shops closed early.

On Thursday, a technical engineer from Tilehurst took his motorbike instead of his car to work at Woodley aerodrome, telling his wife he could see better on the bike. Just fifteen minutes later he collided with a lorry at Earley and died of his injuries.

On Friday and over the weekend there was a spate of minor accidents and AA patrolmen were overwhelmed with enquiries from anxious fogbound drivers who had wandered from their routes.

The *Berkshire Chronicle* reported: "Around Reading's week of almost continuous fog is woven a story of triumph over difficulties. Transport chiefs are warm in their praise for the way in which staffs have battled to keep communications going in the most appalling weather. Drivers, conductors, inspectors and regulators were wonderful as a team."

The fog was a forerunner to a succession of real peasoupers in the early '50's in which the most infamous was the great London water fog of December 1952. Berkshire towns suffered, as they always did, but Londoners who lived along the industrial banks of the Thames were trapped in poisonous pockets and suffered an irritation to their respiratory system caused by the joint effects of sulphur dioxide and smoke. The coughing and vomiting led to heart failure and in two weeks in Greater London, approximately 8,000 people died — nearly double the normal death rate.

Powerful weekend storms and driving snow on the first two days of 1949 brought flood waters surging back to the Thames Valley, less than two years after the misery and tragedy of the winter of 1947. The floods spread through the lower reaches of the Thames and areas around Abingdon, Wallingford, Sonning, Wargrave, Henley, Cookham, Maidenhead, Windsor and Eton were extensively inundated. Picture shows the drama at Wargrave where the water threatened to completely submerge these homes.

1950 — 1959

The road to Wantage blocked by drifting snow in January 1954.

1950: The longest tornado in Britain and one of the most destructive began in Berkshire on 21st May, 1950. It travelled a distance of 100 miles.

1951: A heavy storm in the Wallingford area on 7th September brought dramatic thunder and vivid lightning. Houses and trees were struck with 1.75 inches of rain falling.

1952: A return to winter took place at the end of March with the coldest late March day for 82 years on Saturday 29th, accompanied by gale force north-east winds and driving snow. Sonning was virtually isolated and roads around Newbury saw teams of snow ploughs in what were described as chaotic conditions.

The Reading Co-operative Society choir were victims of the snow storm. After giving a concert to inmates at Broadmoor,Crowthorne, they left by coach mid-evening and soon became stuck fast in the snow. Despite all efforts the coach could not be moved and the choir members trudged through the snow to Wokingham and from there made it to Reading in the early hours — still singing!

1953: Coronation Day was dismal, damp and cold, though this did not stop people celebrating. However, swimming events at Thameside Promenade in Reading were only for the brave. Christmas was one of the mildest on record and so fine and warm that people were seen to be strolling along without overcoats. Temperatures reached the low 50s Fahrenheit.

1954: A gale on January 15th tore off a large factory roof at Theale, wrecking two cars parked adjacent to it. The weather then became very much colder and by the 28th there were 16 degrees of frost, following about four inches of snow, accompanied by a sharp easterly wind. This caused a spate of frozen pipes, including locomotives at Reading Station whose pipes from water tank to boiler froze, something which the station master, Mr Holmes, had not experienced in his 46 years of service. The Salvation Army bandsmen could not play their instruments at St Mary Butts Church because of ice formation and there was a six inch coating of ice around filters at Fobney and Southcote Water Works.

A severe gale on November 28th, accompanied by 1.7ins (43mm) of rain caused widespread damage. Wokingham Football Club's new stand was blown onto the adjacent railway track, blocking both lines. As soon as it was cleared another furious gust blew further debris onto the line, blocking it again.

1955: A year with 36 days of snow cover at Woolhampton. Snowflakes whirled around in a biting wind as late as 17th May and the temperature fell below freezing at Abingdon. July, however, was warm and almost rainless with only 0.1 inches (3mm) recorded at Woolhampton where the mercury topped 87F (30.6C).

1956: A very cold February with the average temperature below freezing and snow covering the ground for half the month in places. It was, however, very dry with only 0.15 inches of rain (4mm) at Hurley and a spring rainfall (March to May) of just 2.14 inches (55mm) at Shinfield. Unfortunately the summer was poor and August was a disappointment as the mercury hardly reached 70F (21C). It was a white Christmas Day with snow several inches deep.

1957: The mildest March of the century with temperatures more than 6F (4C) above average at Shinfield. The thermometer topped 91F at Finchampstead on 29th June and the sun shone for

(continued on page 83)

Old Father Thames flooded Old Windsor in an inundation reminiscent of the days of old! This was the scene which greeted the photographer on 14th February, 1950 after the river, swollen by heavy rains, had overrun its banks.

Tornado leaves long trail of destruction

21st May, 1950

KNOWN as the Berkshire tornado because it developed in the county, this was one of the extraordinary weather events of the century. The day was a particularly stormy one and rain of tropical force, accompanied by large hailstones, fell in North Berkshire. In Wallington, an inch fell in 1 hours and in Wantage it was the most torrential rainstorm the town had ever experienced. Business premises in Grove Street, Wallingford Street and Mill Street were badly flooded.

The tornado driven by strong Force 6 winds, started near Wallingford and swept along a 100-mile path. It felled five large trees at Wendover and raised a column of water from a nearby canal. At Ashton Clinton, the funnel cloud was seen to be following a zig-zag track and there was severe damage in the village. A brick barn was demolished at Puttenham, an eight-year-old girl was swept away by flood water at Podington in Bedfordshire and two men were killed by lightning at Houghton Conquest. At Linslade, 50 roofs in the town were damaged and a bakery was completely demolished. As the tornado raced on, greenhouses were shattered, crops destroyed, poultry killed and orchards ruined. In the Fens many roads were flooded. At Blakeney in Norfolk the tornado petered out and disappeared over the sea.

The view from the air after the Thames and the Loddon, swollen by many days of rain, burst their banks at Wargrave. Fields were more than five feet deep in low-lying places. During the days immediately after 9th January, 1951 the residents of Wargrave undertook their shopping trips by boat.

Children skating on Christchurch meadows, Reading, beside the Thames in January 1954.

FIVE INFAMOUS BERKSHIRE WINTERS

1890: The coldest December on record, with an average temperature of 30F(-1C) and there was a frost every day in Maidenhead. On 14th December in Reading the temperature failed to rise above 21F(-6C) and during the whole winter there were 36 days when it failed to rise above freezing. Frost penetrated to over a foot into the ground.

1895: The coldest February since 1855 with an average temperature of 28F(-2C). With little snow and temperatures down to near zero Fahrenheit, frost penetrated to almost two feet in places. It was a glorious time for skaters with ice well over six inches thick on rivers and lakes. However, innumerable water pipes froze and in towns such as Reading there was a serious water shortage with 12 water carts and some 100 men employed as carriers. In Scotland a temperature of -17F(-27C) was recorded, the lowest official temperature in Britain at the time, equalled in January 1982.

1940: January was the coldest month since 1895 with an average temperature of 30F(-1C) at Reading. Rivers became icebound. One of the most unusual aspects of this severe spell was an ice storm which affected parts of the south of England on the 27th. Supercooled rain fell which immediately froze, coating all objects in an icy filigree which soon became an unbearable mantle, splintering and cracking trees, bringing down miles of telephone lines and even ice-welding sheep to hedges by their frozen fleeces.

1947: The coldest February of the century. The very cold winter began late, not until the third week of January but continued into March. Nationally, four million sheep and lambs were lost, 50,000 head of cattle died of hunger or cold, 40,000 tons of potatoes in clamps were destroyed and a further 35,000 tons washed away by the ensuing floods. 60,000 acres of winter corn were cut down by the perils of frost, snow and floods. The National Farmers Union estimated the losses at £20 million.

1963: The coldest winter since 1740. The ground was covered in snow on 62 mornings at Letcombe Regis, often over a foot deep. A pre-war Austin Seven was driven over the ice-bound Thames at Oxford. At one stage, more than 95,000 miles of roads were reported snowbound from Cornwall to Perthshire and a farm on Dartmoor, cut off by 20-foot drifts, was relieved by troops after 66 days on March 2nd. In Berkshire, Compton had an average January temperature of only 25F(-4C). In February it was 29F(-2C), more akin to winter conditions in Poland.

What better way to quicken the course of the blood on the coldest Easter of the century than to go for a 50-mile walk? The 600 'hard-core' marchers set out to achieve this on 7th April, 1958 in a rally organised by the new Campaign for Nuclear Disarmament. In bitterly cold weather with flurries of snow the anti-hydrogen bomb protesters walked from London to Aldermaston where they are seen arriving on 8th April. They were joined by 12,000 supporters at the gates of the Atomic Weapons Research Establishment. The crowd was mostly made up of students and young parents who heard speeches from pacifists from England, Germany and America. They passed a resolution urging Britain and the two super powers to stop the manufacture, testing and storage of nuclear weapons. It was a peaceful protest.

1950 — 1959 (cont)

more than ten hours a day at Abingdon in June. Winds gusted to nearly 70 mph in a severe gale on 4th November.

1958: A remarkable change in fortunes during January. A bitterly cold northerly airstream sent the temperature down to 16F(-9C) at Abingdon on 24th but this was quickly replaced by a southerly wind on 27th and the temperature soared to 57F(14C). There was further snow and cold for a time in late February and Easter was the coldest of the century with the mercury down to 25F(-4C) at Finchampstead on 2nd April with several inches of snow. The year as a whole was wet (33.2 inches of rain at Hurley) and in an inauspicious summer, one of the best days of the year was as early as 2nd May, when the temperature in many places exceeded 77F(25C).

1959: Thick fog in early February forced one woman to abandon her car. She had had dinner at a house in Warfield and set off with four gallons in the tank. By 3am, having driven round in circles totally lost, she ran out of petrol. Fortunately she managed to rouse a local farmer and spent the rest of the night on a couch. She had little idea where she had left the car. After the fog had lifted it was traced to Winkfield Lane near Bracknell. Finchampstead was the warmest place in Britain during May when the temperature soared to 82F on the 12th. It was a long, hot summer during which work began on the headquarters of the meteorological office at Bracknell. This was a busy time for Bracknell fire brigade who dealt with 203 emergencies due to the heat. In 1958 there had only been 92 calls. Abingdon measured 93F (34C) on 5th July. September was virtually rainless and 80F was reached as late as 3rd October. On 9th July large hail fell at Wokingham.

High summer on the Berkshire Downs in the late 1950's. This is the view towards the ancient Ridgeway which runs along the crest of the Downs. The clump of trees is known as Sparsholt Firs. The Berkshire Downs are renowned worldwide as a training area for racehorses.

At last — a summer to write about!

THE summer of 1959 was one of the sunniest of the century with many places receiving no rain at all between 14th August and 10th October. In Berkshire the memorable weather began in May when the temperature soared into the eighties — in fact on 12th May, Finchampstead was declared the warmest place in Britain. The sun shone throughout July, with 93F (34C) at Abingdon and continued through August while September was virtually rainless.

On 7th August, the *Berkshire Chronicle* described the summer of 1959 as the most satisfying for a whole decade. "Since 1949 we've heard the mournful cry — 'what has happened to the English summer', those halcyon days which elderly people purport to remember as commonplace in their youth.

"This year came the return of the sun with parched lawns and drooping flowers and leaves tumbling from the limes long before the accustomed fall. Ascot and Henley and many humble fetes on vicarage lawns have revelled in the largesse of the gods."

The newspaper posed the question: "Why such a long succession of grey and weeping days in the prvious years?" Was it caused, as so many believed, by the nuclear explosions, or by the onset of a new glacial age which thousands of years ago brought the Arctic cap south of Durham? Or was the old English summer no more than a nostalgic vision of the ageing mind? The answer, of course, was simple. It was not due either to a glacial or an atomic age. The English climate had always been intensely variable.

1960 — 1969

Henley's Royal regatta enjoyed another sparkling decade culminating in the brilliant sunshine of July 1969.

1960: Deep snow in mid-January but by 28th the mercury peaked at 60F. A severe storm on 22nd June in the north west of the county resulted in 1.93 inches of rain at Abingdon. A very cool summer saw the mercury fall below average every day in July at Compton with a maximum of 72F (22C) and only 73F (23C) during August. On 14th June, during a severe thunderstorm, a gardener from Church Road, Bracknell had a lucky escape when the bough of a tree crashed through the hut he had just vacated. The tree had been split from top to bottom by lightning. An extraordinarily wet autumn followed with 8.43 inches(215mm) of rain at Woolhampton during October.

1961: Young love received just the tonic on Valentine's Day with a very warm 62F (17C) at Hurley. March was virtually rainless except for 0.04 inches at Finchampstead on 31st and damaging frosts late in May gave credibility to the adage, "Ne'er cast a clout 'til May be out", the mercury falling to 27F (-3C) at Wallingford on 28th. The summer ended in a heatwave with 89F (32C) on 29th August at Abingdon and by 1st September the temperature was still no lower than 87F (31C) at Letcombe Regis. In contrast the year ended in cold, snowy conditions of 10F (-12C) and the Thames was frozen over at Reading.

1962: A very chilly start to a cold year with just 1F (-17C) at Wallingford in early January. On the 11th gusts up to 72 mph were recorded at Abingdon. There was an air frost on 1st June — 28F (-2C) at Wallingford and the mercury did not rise above 75F (24C) at Compton all summer. Bank holiday was a washout in August with 3.22 inches(82mm) of rain

at Wallingford, the coldest and wettest since 1888. Spring was the coldest of the century and the year the bleakest since 1919. Dense fog obscured 4th - 6th December and it was the chilliest Christmas since 1897 with deep snow by 27th and a blizzard on 29th.

1963: At Letcombe Regis snow covered the ground throughout January and February in what was the coldest winter since 1740. On 23rd January the temperature fell to 3F (-16C) at Compton and the average reading for the month was 28F (-2C) at Reading. The mercury remained below freezing for 238 consecutive hours from noon on 16th January to 10am on 26th. A post office worker sprained his ankle on the way to work when he tried to free his car from a snow drift south of Maidenhead. His name was Jack Frost! Men were sent home with half a hair cut as power cuts plunged shoppers into confusion, and in Bracknell a plumber had 81 calls in 36 hours because of burst pipes. A dramatic year reached its zenith with tornadoes reported on 2nd September.

1964: This was generally the driest winter in 250 years, since rainfall readings were first compiled. Many parts of Berkshire had only 2 inches (50mm) of rain in the three months. The annual rainfall at Abingdon amounted to only 15.92 inches (407mm), although a deluge during Royal Ascot led to the abandonment of part of the programme.

1965: A splendid display of haloesround the sun could be seen across the county during the evening of 11th, some very rare. Colours were vivid with arcs of red and green, yellow and orange. High cirrus clouds composed of ice crystals were responsible. March was a Jekyll and Hyde month with a snow storm on the 4th bringing deep drifts to the Downs. However, there was a taste of summer at the end of the month when the thermometer reached nearly 73F(23C) at Bracknell.

1966: An exceptionally cold spell in mid-January brought temperatures as low as 11F (-12C) at Letcombe Regis, while a predicted snowstorm turned to freezing rain causing chaos across the county. Milder weather followed and there was no snow until mid April when several inches fell on the 14th, registering a midday temperature of freezing point.

1967: An observer at Bracknell claimed to have smelt a distinct odour of crude oil on Easter Monday. Winds were blowing from the direction of the Torrey Canyon, wrecked on the Seven Stones Reef off Lands End. A blizzard on 8th December blocked roads on the Berkshire Downs and Wallingford was the coldest place in England this year at 8F (-13C).

1968: A year that brought everything from a technicolour dust-fall straight from the Sahara in June, a temperature as high as 91F (33C) at Shinfield, to deep snow in January and remarkable deluges such as the 3.79 inches (97mm) that fell at Letcombe Regis on 10th July and the 2.6 inches (66mm) at Finchampstead on 15th September. Snow fell on Christmas night and covered the ground in parts of the county.

1969: A bitterly cold spell at the end of November plunged temperatures on the grass to just 9F (-13C) on the 30th. Snow had fallen the previous day in the east of the county and the sunset was a delicate greenish hue. Traces of snow were to be found on trees still partly in leaf due to an unusually warm and dry October which at Wallingford saw only 0.1 inch (3mm) of rain fall.

January, 1960 and a frost hard enough to freeze many Berkshire rivers. The young man stepping warily across the Kennet and Avon Canal at Thatcham is David Canning who has supplied several photographs for this book. This was the prelude to one of the coldest decades of the century with snow falling every year but one. The infamous winter of 1963 was destined to be the coldest since 1740.

Coldest winter for 200 years

December 1962 — March 1963

CHRISTMAS 1962 heralded the coldest period of winter weather since 1740. Heavy snow fell on Boxing Day afternoon and lay on the ground for more than two months. Although the winter had plenty of sunshine to give a little alpine cheer to the big freeze, it was generally a time of battling to keep homes warm and factories open.

On Christmas Day, the temperature reached only 33F (1C) in Reading despite five hours of sunshine. That night was very cold indeed. The mercury fell to 19F (-7C) and although Boxing Day dawned fair, to the north west there was already a tell-tale sign in the sky of an impending breakdown in the weather. By the afternoon a veil of cloud had spread over the county and before dusk, heavy snow fell, burying the region in a thick blanket which was four inches deep in Reading.

In spite of the wintry conditions, town traffic was kept moving and there were no delays on Reading's trolley buses. However, around Newbury, some country roads were blocked and the Thames Valley Traction Company found some of their vehicles were suffering from frozen radiators.

By Saturday, 29th December, the River Thames was frozen over for a quarter of a mile stretch at Windsor, but much worse was to occur in the ensuing days. That day, a weather trough moved slowly north towards the Channel in the icy airstream. A severe blizzard followed with fine, powder-like snow smothering everything in its path. Mountainous drifts of snow blocked roads over the Berkshire Downs.

The Berkshire downland villages of Leckhampstead, Chaddleworth and Brightwalton, which all lie between the A338 Wantage-Hungerford road and the B4494 Wantage-Newbury road, were cut off for six days. Snow-ploughs and dozens of council workers toiled for hours to free the snow-bound communities, but with ten inches of level snow and drifts several feet deep it was bound to be a long rescue operation.In North Berkshire, the *Oxford Mail* revealed that the blizzard was the worst since 1881, even though there were heavier falls in 1927, 1942 and 1947.

The *Reading and Berkshire Chronicle* reported on 4th January that "staggering sums of money and huge quantities of material have had to be used in the fight to clear the snow in Reading and Berkshire; villages on the Downs have been isolated; public transport services and motorists have had difficulty in keeping going; milk, paraffin and vegetables have been in short supply. It is just a small part of the picture presented by this week of Arctic conditions". The Southern Region of British Railways operated a skeleton service in the hope that this could be run to time, but on the roads the situation was grim. In the first stage of the big freeze, Berkshire County Council had spent nearly £60,000 on snow clearance, using 7,000 tons of grit and 2.500 tons of salt.

One clearance gang team working between Wantage and Newbury were themselves trapped by the snow on New Year's Eve. After spending the night in the open they were rescued and one was taken to hospital suffering from exposure. On the A338 Wantage to Hungerford Road, a snow-plough struggled through but, together with a gritting lorry, had to be abandoned. The crew of the plough and lorry made several attempts to get through to a bus stranded since 30th December. The driver, conductor and passengers continued their journey on a farm trailer.

It was not just motorists who had to be rescued. The RSPCA had to save swans from frozen lakes and ponds around the county.

Major milk suppliers were worried about the scarcity of milk bottles, for householders were not leaving them out and if they did, they were becoming buried in the snow and difficult to find. As a result " in some cases the housewife has to be content with about half the milk she usually gets". Village shopkeepers reported a boost in business, for customers were not going far afield because of the difficulties in travelling. One Reading baker had to work overtime to cope with the demand. Sales of paraffin doubled and an acute shortage was experienced as the inclement weather continued. Coal and coke supplies got through but there were some delays. However, the situation was not nearly as bad as in the winter of 1947.

On Wednesday, 2nd January, the Royal Automobile Association reported that among the roads still blocked were the Newbury-Hungerford road and the Wantage-Newbury road over the Downs. At Pangbourne, police directed Newbury-bound traffic along the A340 on to the Bath Road at Theale to avoid blocked downland routes, and on the A417 Wantage-Faringdon route, only heavy lorries with chains on their wheels could get through. The Abingdon-Kingston-Bagpuize road was also impassable for several days.

Catmore, Stanmore, Farnborough, Fawley and Combe were isolated for the best part of a week. A similar picture emerged from the villages of Berrick Salome and Brightwell Baldwin near Watlington, where roads were buried under nine foot snowdrifts.

On 3rd January, the situation deteriorated. More than three inches of fresh snow fell in North Berkshire, blocking the A34 Abingdon-Newbury route and the A329 Shillingford-Reading road in addition to the other hilly highways still affected. "More snow fell in the night, in malicious partnership with a high wind which piled up more drifts to undo much of the work done by local authority workmen everywhere," reported the *Oxford Mail.* Demand for electricity was

The River Kennet, frozen at Newbury in January 1963

exceptional and a reduced supply was threatened unless consumers cut down. Virtually all sport was wiped out by the worst weather the south has known "for nearly 100 years," the *Reading Chronicle* stated.

On 4th January, the Wantage to Hungerford main road which was blocked and led to eight or more Berkshire villages being cut off for six days, was opened up but the Wantage to Newbury road over the hills was still out of reach. A farm tractor laden with fresh food managed to locate the 200 stricken villagers in Combe earlier the same day while the snowbound communities in Chaddleworth, Brightwalton, Leckhampstead, Fawley and Farnborough were freed the following day.

Temperatures throughout January stayed mostly below freezing by day and night, and any excursions of the mercury above freezing point were soon terminated. The Thames was almost frozen over at Caversham Bridge while in Wargrave, snow ploughs battled to clear the High Street of tons of snow. In spite of the cutting frosts, there were no more significant snowfalls until 19th January. In one snow shower on Wednesday, 16th January, however, an American Air Force officer was killed in an accident on the Twyford-Henley road near Marsh Mills, and seven hours later, two Tilehurst men died in another collision involving a coach on the Bath Road at Sonning. One of the dead men had been married for just two weeks.

Schoolchildren greeted the icy weather "joyously" for Christmas holidays were extended in some areas whilst in others, school hours were reduced because toilets had frozen up. British Railways Western Region complained of the wrong type of weather for testing out their new anti-freeze oil for points. The experiments were due to be carried out at Didcot but because of deep snow the trial had to be abandoned. An earlier attempt at trying out the liquid had also proved fruitless because the weather was too warm!

A northerly wind was blamed for blowing back coke fumes into Holy Trinity Church, Theale, on 13th January, resulting in several people collapsing and being taken to hospital during a sermon by the Bishop of Reading. The Bishop said afterwards he had also been feeling "a bit shaky" but decided to continue with Communion. Three people were taken home by ambulance and 17 recovered after first aid. Among the victims was the verger. The Bishop himself raised the alarm by driving to Theale police station and calling for ambulances.

By 18th January, the Thames had frozen over completely at both Reading and Windsor. At Reading, Thames Conservancy vessels cut through the ice to keep the navigational channels open and prevent people from trying to walk on it. Danger signs were put up on tripods near Reading bridge. Skaters took to Queensmere Lake near Wokingham, the more experienced jumping over marker buoys, used in warmer times by a boating club.

On 1st February, the *Chronicle* told how 2,486 people had been put out of work by the cold spell in January and 24,000 had been forced to go part-time. The newspaper also told how burst pipes had flooded cellars around the region after a brief thaw. The thaw, however, did not last more than a few hours and February remained very cold and frosty with some more snow at times.

The coldest winter for 223 years gradually gave way to milder, conditions in early March, but for many, it remained etched on their minds for years to come.

In Reading the snow got the better of even the indomitable Mini, a car that could get through better than most with its front-wheel drive.

The Thames, frozen from bank to bank at Windsor. This picture of grateful swans being fed was taken on 22nd January 1963 looking downstream towards the Eton-Windsor Road bridge.

A reflective Newbury in the sunshine of high summer, August 1966.

Spanish dust falls in technicolour

1st July, 1968

"THE rain from Spain fell mainly in technicolour this morning. Red, pink, beige, rust-coloured and white showers washed over cars and windows and left their crusty mark." So said the front page of the *Evening Post* after the sensational dust storm of 1st July, 1968.

This unusual phenomenon came with high temperature, low humidity and warm winds which carried sand and dust from northern Africa and Spain to a great height and then deposited it. This dust fall wasn't confined to Berkshire. It covered an area from the Channel Islands to north Yorkshire and as far west as the mountains of Wales.

There was, however, great confusion in the county over the exact colour of the fall-out. A wide area of East Berkshire went pink, said the police. In Bracknell, it was beige reported housewives. Caversham greeted the dawn with an inscrutable yellow while other places saw red, white and brown deposits on their cars.

The Met. office at Bracknell had an explanation. "The dirty rain was the result of thunderstorms in the Bay of Biscay which had originated in Spain or Morocco and were now moving through England. The air where these storms came from was dusty and the soil very dry. This accounted for the deposits. The phenomenon was unusual but not unknown."

When the rains came down

14th-15th September, 1968

ON Saturday afternoon, 14th September, 1968 a thunderstorm boomed across the Downs and valleys of Berkshire followed by an almost Stygian gloom and heavy rain. The culprit was a rapidly deepening depression to the south-west of Britain which had produced a pronounced trough of low pressure. Along this trough were large scale vertical motions of the atmosphere and it remained stationary all day. A warning went out from weather stations; beware of heavy rain.

It was somewhat of an understatement. A few hours later, the rain had turned into a monsoon of tropical proportions. Hour after hour it pelted down, transforming streams and brooks into wild raging torrents and sending riverside dwellers into a frenzy as they moved furniture to upstairs rooms in preparation for the worst.

Some 24 hours later Berkshire was awash. Families were marooned, cars abandoned, road and rail services in chaos, towns and villages cut off. Firemen spent most of Sunday night pumping water out of the Tesco supermarket in Bell Street, Henley. Householders in Upper Warren Avenue, Caversham were fighting in vain to stop dirty floodwater swamping their homes. Slough was completely under water and a block of flats at Gough's Meadows, Sandhurst had to be evacuated. The Berkshire and Reading Fire Service said it was impossible to count the number of calls for assistance.

The worst affected places were Wokingham, Ascot, Crowthorne, Bracknell and Newbury. Passengers at Newbury railway station ran for higher ground when water poured out of the drains and swept across the platform filling the cutting. Between Maidenhead and Wycombe several cars were abandoned. The A423 between Maidenhead and Henley and the A308 at Bullocks Hatch Bridge, near Bray looked more like a tributary of the Thames.

The fear of vast flooding grew on Monday as the rivers continued to rise. Only at Wokingham was there any sign of joy and that was confined to the 460 pupils at Emmbrook County Secondary whose school was flooded. At Sandhurst, the rural council surveyor said that three inches of rain had fallen in 38 hours. "It was fantastic."

On Tuesday the situation had worsened. At Twyford motorists were locked in an 18-mile queue stretching from the village towards Wokingham and both AA and RAC patrols were pulling out flooded casualties as quickly as they could. Warnings went out to keep away from the area, for main roads were flooded with a foot of water. By now many communities were cut off including Warfield, Sunningdale, Winnersh, Arborfield and Swallowfield. Staff at The George public house by the River Loddon at Woodley had to paddle through water behind the public bar to serve customers. The lounge bar was evacuated.

Many factories were flooded, including the C.F.Taylor group at Wokingham. Here production came to a halt but, worse still, the design plans for the new Concorde aircraft were badly damaged and drawing office workers had to be sent home.

The drama was not confined to Berkshire. Hampshire, Sussex, Kent, Essex and Suffolk were badly hit and it was estimated that more than 1,000 square miles were under water. Some places recorded as much as a third of their annual rainfall in two days; totals of five inches or more were recorded on Sunday, alone.

An intrepid photographer at Lands End, Charvil.

A day off school! The children of Wokingham were delighted. This was 16th September, 1968.

Newbury didn't escape. This was the scene on the same day.

1970 — 1979

Shottesbrooke Church, near Maidenhead, in March 1970.

1970: Nearly four inches of snow fell on 4th March at Abingdon and the next morning the mercury dropped to just 18F (-8C). At Hurley the temperature fell below freezing on 16 nights during March. A thunderstorm on 7th August at Harwell produced 2.54 inches (65mm) of rain in 81 minutes. Meteorologically this is a very rare event in Britain, as such a fall is expected to occur at any one place on average once in every 160 years. Christmas was white in many parts of Berkshire owing to a shallow area of low pressure. On 28th December the mercury dropped to 17F (-8C) at Wallingford.

1971: A mild January with the temperature reaching almost 57F (14C) on the 10th at Easthampstead. May was a lovely month with nearly 250 hours of sunshine in Reading but June was a disappointment with frequent downpours and a monthly rainfall three and a half times more than average. August, too, was dismal with only 120 hours of sun at Hurley. The balance was restored in November, however, as the sun shone for more than 100 hours and new records were achieved in some places.

1972: Across much of Berkshire the mercury had failed to rise above 70F (21C) by the end of June. Excessive sea-ice off Newfoundland was the probable cause for the latter part of the month being cool and unsettled.

1973: There were some deluges in what turned out to be the driest year since 1964. On 6th October, as a trough of low pressure moved north from Spain, 1.6 inches of rain (40mm) fell in just 35 minutes during a thunderstorm at Taplow Court. This was about two thirds of the monthly average rainfall.

1974: Reading had the wettest year since 1970 with more than 31 inches of rain. December was actually milder than October, something that may not have occurred since 1673.

1975: Easter was cold with wintry showers and temperatures in early April down to 24F (-5C). Orchards which had blossomed early after a mild winter were damaged by frost. August, over England as a whole, was the warmest in 300 years of records. Shinfield measured 93F(34C) on 4th and the daily temperature rose on average to 77F(25C) during the month. Easthampstead recorded the lowest temperature in England during this year with a low of 14F(-10C) on 16th December.

1976: A year remembered for its long, hot summer in which a main newspaper headline was, "Blazing Berkshire". Huge fires raged such as the one at Padworth where scores of homes were threatened and firemen fought day and night to avert disaster. Temperatures soared to 95F (35C). From January to the end of August only six inches(155mm) of rain fell at Sandhurst, about a third of the expected quantity. The appointment of a Minister of Drought on St Swithin's Day had the desired effect. The autumn was the fourth wettest on record.

1977: A very mixed summer. Jubilee Day on 6th June was cool and showery and the month brought some heavy thunderstorms. On the night of 13th/14th lightning caused a disruption to computer operations at the meteorological headquarters at Bracknell. It was a very dull month with many completely cloudy days and only 120 hours of sun compared to an average of nearly 200. July was dry, only 0.4 inches (10mm) of rain fell in most places whereas August brought frequent deluges. On the 16th, Hurley measured three inches (74mm) of rain.

1978: A remarkable October. A mere 0.07 inch (2mm)of rain fell at Bracknell, a fraction more at Wokingham and the mercury reached 75F (24C) on the 12th. During the evening and night of 30th December and on New Year's Eve, heavy snow fell producing ten foot drifts. On the last day of 1978 the temperature did not rise above 27F (-3C).

1979: During the coldest January and February since 1963 snow covered the ground on half the days in parts of Bracknell where there was a most curious fall of ice crystals during the late morning of 27th January. The temperature at the time was 24F (-4C). A tornado struck Eton and Windsor on 21st June. The flooding of the Thames at Abingdon in late December was regarded as the worst in 25 years.

1970 — a classic White Christmas...

HERE was a rare event in Berkshire — snow on Christmas Day. Several inches fell in the early hours of the morning and much of the county, particularly in the north, was covered with a white mantle, just like the pictures on Christmas cards.

Children who lived in the villages on the Downs were especially delighted and quickly pulled their toboggans to the hillsides. This is what grandad had told them was a common occurrence earlier in the century. It was "just like the ones I used to know". The words of the song had come true at last.

The novelty of snow lasted over the holiday period and then, as the temperature plunged to 18F (-8C) at Abingdon came the great struggle to get to work. On lethal roads there were scores of accidents and the AA reported 859 breakdown calls in the five days immediately after Christmas.

The White Christmas babes of 1970 with their mums at Reading General Hospital.

Just like the ones we used to know...

1906: Snow began to fall around 11 pm on Christmas night after a crisp, clear cold sunset which brought the temperature down to 21F (-6C). On Boxing Day morning the whole county was covered in a thick mantle — over six inches deep in places.

1927: A fierce snowstorm began during Christmas evening and continued through much of Boxing Day. The snow was accompanied by gale force winds piling up huge drifts. Massive corniced, wonderfully sculptured drifts overhung the Theale to Pangbourne Road and the Wallingford to Henley Road had the appearance of a trench flanked by towering icy walls many feet high.

1938: After an extremely mild November and first half of December in which the temperatures actually reached the middle fifties, a severe cold and penetrating easterly wind set in and it snowed virtually every day from 8th to 26th. Around Newbury snow was a foot deep and everywhere there were scenes such as those depicted on the most traditional of Christmas cards.

1956: A weather system moving in from the west came up against a cold south-east airstream and rain in the west turned to snow in Berkshire on Christmas night, giving a covering of between two and four inches by Boxing Day morning.

1968: A depression moved across the West Country bringing rain which turned to snow over parts of Berkshire on Christmas Eve. Many people woke up to a festive covering of several inches.

1970: Snow showers fell on Christmas Eve, swept in by a very cold north-east airstream from Scandinavia. By Christmas morning many parts were snow-covered and it remained snowy for the rest of the month. Temperatures never rose above freezing on Christmas Day on the Berkshire Downs.

June 1971 failed to blaze. In fact it was so wet that the average rainfall in Berkshire was more than three times normal. In these conditions there were flash floods and here Jeffrey Cohen of Southcote Manor, Hartford Road, Reading finds the ideal way to get around.

Hundreds of trees toppled in a great gale on 2nd — 3rd January 1976. The Newbury manager of SEB described it as the worst wind in memory; it brought down 179 power lines serving 5,500 customers and linesmen from all over the country were drafted in to repair the damage. Some homes were without power for three days. One victim was the great yew in Aldworth churchyard which was reputed to be 1,000 years old (see page 5). The picture was taken in the south of the county at Sulhamstead Hill

The blazing summer of '76

DENSE smoke rose high into the summer sky as flames engulfed fields and woods all over the county. Firemen worked round the clock as fresh fires raged. This was a nightmare that few would have thought possible in our normally green and pleasant land but the summer of 1976 was no ordinary summer.

After a dry winter and spring an unprecedented heatwave which began in earnest on 23rd June brought such a long period of high temperatures that the countryside became tinder dry waiting for a carelessly dropped cigarette or a sliver of glass to focus the sun's rays.

Such a scenario took place at Nutfield House, Henley. A fire started in the grounds of the house owned by the mother of MP Michael Heseltine. In no time flames had swept across parched fields fanned by a strong wind. Mr Heseltine arrived home and tried to quell the blaze but to no avail. The Abrahams Estate and Badgemore Farm now lay in its path. Scores of housewives formed a human chain passing pots and buckets of water to help firemen who had arrived on the scene. They doused the fence surrounding the estate and probably prevented a worse disaster. As it was, two outbuildings on the farm were destroyed and crops on allotments perished before the situation was brought under control.

It was a torrid time for firemen. Infernos were breaking out all over the county and crews were put on constant alert, fighting fires for 14 hours at a time. Some even gave up their holidays as calls averaged more than 100 a day. Some fire fighters were almost camping out in places such as Swinley Forest where smouldering peat and leaves constantly re-ignited. Troops were called in to help and "Green Goddess" auxiliary appliances were borrowed from Home Office stores at Didcot. At Woodbrook Common near Maidenhead, crops were lost in a large blaze. Another incident saw a 25 acre woodland destroyed at Mortimer. Part of Newbury Racecourse Station was gutted and there were more blazes at Hermitage and Bucklebury.

The alarming situation can be explained by going back to the 1960's when periods of high pressure were on the increase. These gave rise to long spells of dry weather, intensified during the next decade. The years of 1972 and 1973 were both dry although the following year turned out wet despite a dry spring when only 1.7 inches (43mm) of rain was recorded. 1975 is remembered for a dry, hot summer and the following winter and spring exacerbated the situation. Then came a dramatic surge of heat when the average maximum temperature from 23rd June to 8th July approached a staggering 90F (32C) with around 13 hours of sunshine a day.

At Wimbledon during the tennis championship 2,700 people suffered sunburn and dehydration! Drier soils than average, warmer seas and the high altitude of the sun around the summer solstice, all contributed to an outstanding heatwave.

Meanwhile the causes were no consolation to the people of Padworth, Ufton Nervet and Aldermaston, for here were the most widespread and frightening of the conflagrations. 100 firemen from five counties fought for two days to stem the flames. Villagers were evacuated as fire encircled homes and a thick, black pall of smoke hung over the area. Many never expected to see their homes again and an emergency centre was established in Padworth Village Hall.

A peaceful Sunday lunch was suddenly shattered for the residents of Pinelands Caravan Site when flames engulfed nearby trees. Almost at once firemen rushed in and told people to evacuate the area. Smoke and flames filled the air and they were led away in shock, having no time to take any of their possessions. Amazingly, they returned later in the day to find their homes saved.

Back at Padworth, an oil storage depot was threatened and 16 fire appliances fought to save valuable houses. They even had to pump water from the River Kennet when local supplies failed. A dutch barn holding 150 tons of hay worth £3,000 went up in flames and a cottage in Rectory Road was damaged, the occupant being taken to hospital.

The drought, which continued through August, was producing a very serious situation and drastic measures were being contemplated by the government on top of the hosepipe bans already imposed.

Water levels were running very low. At Wallingford a farm and 16 houses saw their supplies totally dry up as a bore hole failed for the first time and the River Thames at its source, dried up for a length of more than ten miles. Fifteen million gallons a day was soaking away from its bed due to the excessive drop in the water table. The cost of loss of crops alone in England was put at £500 million.

Nationally, the seriousness of the circumstances was illustrated by the Drought Bill published on 15th July and the appointment of a drought minister, Mr Dennis Howell. More stringent restrictions on the use of water were announced, temporary pipelines planned, tankers were to carry emergency water supplies, existing bore holes were to be deepened and generally water conservation was encouraged.

However, the day of the appointment was inspired, for it was St Swithin's Day and rain did fall in places and although the legend of abundant rainfall did not immediately come true, the autumn that followed was the fourth wettest on record since 1727. The problem was simply washed away.

Spring 1976 and the forerunner to one of the most memorable summers of the century. Here the Rt.Hon. Dennis Howell MP, aboard the narrow boat 'Slough', appraches Towney Lock, near Newbury to perform the official opening of that stretch of the Kennet and Avon Canal. This was part of an enterprising restoration programme involving all 87 miles of the badly neglected canal between Reading and Bristol. This picture was taken on 26th May and within a few weeks the temperature had hit the nineties, water was at a premium and rivers and reservoirs were suffering all the symptoms associated with an unprecedented heatwave — until the water-loving Dennis Howell was appointed Minister of Drought. Within weeks, rain was pelting down. and the autumn that followed was one of the wettest on record.

THE WINDSOR
SLOUGH EXPRESS—PART 2
AND ETON

FRIDAY, AUGUST 27, 1976

SPORT 18, 19; NEWS 20, 21, 22
CLASSIFIED INDEX 29
TV & LEISURE 32

TOO MANY FIRES—TOO LITTLE WATER

TURN OFF OR DRY UP

TURN OFF or dry up — that is the message from the Middle Thames Water Authority this week as the drought gets steadily worse.

The authority, which serves the Slough area, is appealing to everybody to cut their water consumption by 50 per cent.

"People seem to have cut their water consumption by about 15 per cent now," a spokesman told the Express. "This is good but we would like to see it down even more."

There is a shortage of water throughout the Thames Valley, which is expected to get worse next month when consumption usually rises as people return from holiday.

"It cannot go on forever. You cannot supply a commodity which is not being replaced."

Stage one of the Drought Act, which will give the authority new powers to ban the watering of parks, sports grounds, golf courses, etc and bring in other water saving restrictions is expected to come into force locally on September 3.

"But anyone still watering parks and so on is totally anti-social," said the spokesman. "Nobody should be that anti-social that they are still watering."

He said the authority has received various complaints about people's neighbours watering their gardens, but is not encouraging this spying.

Crackdown on water wasters

MIDDLE Thames Water Authority has begun to crack down on people who have been ignoring the current ban on the use of garden hoses, sprinklers and ban. Where staff are available, all reports are followed up.

But just now the authority admits it is powerless to take action against a number of golf clubs, bowling greens and other sports associations which con-

"This is now on the table but we have to go through the usual procedure of advertising the order through the Press. In the meantime we can only ask them to stop — it is a matter of social responsibility.

BUCKS Fire Service issued an urgent plea to the public to take extra care not to start fires.

Mr Stanley Hunt of the Brigade's Aylesbury headquarters said "The number of fires is causing us so much concern and stretching our resources to the limit."

"We are asking the public to take extra care during picnics and not to start fires."

He also asked that people do not throw lighted cigarettes out of cars.

There have been numerous instances of road-side fires started in this way.

"Even the smallest spark can start a fire in these sort of conditions. Everything is so dry," said Mr Hunt.

Mr Hunt is also appealing to farmers to be more vigilant when they burn off crop stubble.

"Some farmers are not abiding by the code of practice for burning stubble," he said. "They are not making fire breaks and the stubble is getting out of control and doing untold damage to property."

"The fire brigade is pleading with farmers to follow the code."

The fires are also damaging the engines. Mr Hunt said: "Our vehicles are built to go over rough ground now and then but not day after day."

Many of the 500 strong brigade have been working a 12 hour day.

"Part-timers are spending more time at fires than in their normal jobs," said Mr Hunt. "Employers are still supporting us as best they can but some are starting to wonder when they will get their employees back."

"Fortunately Bucks has not yet had a job like the Dorset and New Forest Brigades."

He asked that the public be particularly careful in large park areas.

Mr Peter Henton of the High Wycombe and Slough Group of the National Farmers Union said members had been sent a notice asking them not to burn stubble at present.

He said he did not know of any instances when fires had got out of control.

Mr Henton said that if farmers felt they must burn they should plough a strip about 10 yards wide around the area, burn against the wind, never

direct from the Thames. Under the new Act the Middle Thames Water Authority will be able to ban this. The authority will also be able to control the use of private bore holes.

The only exception to the rule

burn at night and never leave the fire un-attended.

The great advantage of burning stubble is the amount of weed control it affords.

AFTER destroying scrubland, two gardens and damaging a pear orchard flames leaped across Parsonage Lane, Farnham Royal, to wreak further havoc in a nursery on the other side of the road.

At 2.30 pm on Sunday the fire broke out in scrubland in Parsonage Lane. It quickly spread to the pear orchard owned by Mr Colin Vanderveil of Brockenhurst Park, Stoke Poges.

While firemen commanding six fire fighting appliances fought to contain the fire, Parsonage Lane was closed to traffic.

Unable to contain the flames the fire spread to the garden of Miss Brooks at Random Stocks, Parsonage Lane, and Mr J. Laine at the Orchard House, destroying both gardens.

The fire then spread across the road, burnt down a hedge and singed crops at Reids Nursery.

Not until 5 pm was the fire brigade able to open Parsonage Lane to traffic again and it was not until 7 pm that the firemen left.

TINDER dry grass on the railway embankment next to Huntercombe Lane North, Burnham caught fire at midday last Wednesday.

There were fears that the fire could spread to the nearby premises of King Brothers Limited, builders, decorators

A FIRE on waste ground in Church Lane, Farnham Royal,

• Cattle is herded away to safety in Black Park as the fire threatens. The blaze, which broke out yesterday, afternoon, affected more than 100 acres of the park and was tackled by firemen from Berks, Bucks and London.

RESIDENTS assisted police to put out a grass fire in a field at the rear of houses in Opendale Road, Burnham on Saturday afternoon. By the time the fire brigade arrived there was nothing left to do.

Drought brings health risk fear to lake

BATHERS have been banned from Black Park's stagnant lake following pollution fears as Slough's drought drags on.

And children have been because of the drought which

The front page of the Windsor, Slough and Eton Express in August 1976. Turn off or dry up, they announced, and don't forget to bath with a friend!

Keeping cool in the summer of 1976. Left an icy drink at Henley. Right, an icy dip at Caversham.

The vagaries of the English climate are clearly shown in this photograph of three young ladies sheltering under umbrellas during the celebrations at Wargrave on 6th June, 1977 to mark the Queen's 25th anniversary. All day it was showery.

The icicles which formed on a tree at Winkworth Lane, Aldermaston during a bitterly cold spell in the second week of February, 1978.

One lane of the M4 motorway was closed to traffic in West Berkshire after the snowstorm of 30th December, 1978. On the Downs there were drifts in excess of 10 feet.

Another great storm on 11th January, 1978, turned Berkshire into a battlefield with hundreds of trees torn out of the ground, thousands of homes left without electricity and widespread damage to property. One of the worst affected areas was around Padworth and Woolhampton in West Berkshire where scores of roads were blocked by fallen trees.

Gale force winds, accompanied by torrential rain, returned at Easter, making the Bank Holiday one of the quietest on record as holidaymakers heeded police warnings and stayed at home.

Fortunately, the deserted roads meant little in the way of traffic accidents but for those who had resigned themselves to a weekend in front of the TV, a different hazard was in store — falling trees. Mr Simon August, a teacher and resident at the Oratory preparatory school, near Streatley, was one of those who had a lucky escape when an uprooted beech tree narrowly missed his bungalow.

By 25th January, 1979 Berkshire was again in the grip of an ice age; in fact January and February were to prove the coldest winter months since the notorious winter of 1963. In these conditions, black ice plagued motorists on the motorway. Many lorries jack-knifed, some skidded and overturned and in others fuel lines froze. Snow was swept into huge drifts as seen in this scene at Brimpton,(above) while children of Maidenhead wasted no time in making a giant snowman.

Two cars, seemingly abandoned, are half submerged in swirling water following one of those great Berkshire monsoon-type deluges which are so famous for producing flash floods. This one occurred early in March, 1979 and this picture was taken at Lands End, near Charvil.

Lightning at Ravenswing during July, 1979.

Firemen from Langley repair a roof at Windsor after the whirlwind.

The day of the whirlwind

24th June 1979

TORNADOES are perhaps the most terrifying weather events. They are also the least merciful. As they sweep through towns, villages and countryside nothing is spared their greed and no-one is safe.

The devastation wrought by a freak whirlwind is always catastrophic So great is their power that miles of countryside can be flattened in a matter of minutes But these mighty storms hold a great fascination too. In the southern states of the USA obsessive "storm chasers" spend three months of the year tracking tornadoes in the hope that they might be "lucky" enough to witness one. Like earthquakes and volcanic eruptions, tornadoes are proof of man's impotence in the face of nature's force.

Tornadoes hold another similarity to earthquakes and volcanoes. They happen elsewhere. In our corner of the world we are safe from such terror.... Or are we?

Just before 10 am on 24th June, 1979, an unusual shape suddenly loomed out of a gloomy Windsor sky. One hundred and fifty feet high and travelling at an estimated speed of 100 mph the funnel-shaped "twister" began to cut a swathe through Berkshire.

This was the "Day of the Whirlwind". It lasted less than three minutes but in that time it travelled five miles and caused £150,000 worth of damage.

The Whiteley housing estate in Windsor was the first place to fall victim to the tornado's might. Hundreds escaped injury as trees were uprooted, greenhouses smashed and tiles and chimneys ripped from roofs. An eight ton lorry, mercifully unattended, was lifted up and thrown on its side.

As quickly as it had begun, the Windsor twister expired at Eton Wick but not before it had destroyed more homes and wrecked a dairy. The next day the *Reading Evening Post* was warning of another whirlwind. It also carried a quote from a resident of Hylle Close, Eton Wick. He said of the event, "I heard a clap of thunder and thought I'd spend the morning in the greenhouse out of the rain. When I got to the garden, my greenhouse was partly standing on top of my neighbour's fence. It had been blown 20 feet by the wind."

Why pick on me? Mr Joe Graham of Hylle Close, Eton Wick wonders why his greenhouse was singled out for special attention by the whirlwind of 24th June, 1979.

The Riverside car park at Wallingford on 30th December, 1979.

Father Thames shows his fury again

29th — 30th December, 1979

THE partial blocking of Boulter's Weir, Maidenhead by a sunken barge which raised water levels as far downstream as Cookham was one of the reasons for the terrible flooding of December 1979 which caught everyone by surprise.

There had been heavy and continuous rain on 27th and 28th December and Thames Water staff responsible for monitoring weather, rainfall and river levels issued flood warnings for the areas that would be affected. The police toured threatened roads with loudhailers. They were just in time, for the swirling, muddy waters overtopped the banks and poured into numerous homes as householders were moving carpets and furniture to upper rooms.

Even so there were flooding incidents from the source of the river to London and a spokesman from Thames Water said it was the most severe flood to affect the whole catchment of the river since 1947.

Maidenhead, Windsor and Eton suffered but the more serious problems were at Purley where many homes had been built on the flood plain.

The great risk of serious flooding, powerfully shown once more, prompted numerous calls to the authorities to devise a scheme to protect towns and villages in the Thames Valley from a flooding disaster. Given the vast amount of development, the cost of flood damage on the scale of 1894 or 1947 was estimated to be in the region of £40 million.

● *A month later, flooding returned to the Thames Valley and a couple were caught up in a chilling nightmare when their car became stranded in a flooded ford at Lands End, Twyford. They abandoned their car, waded through fast-flowing waist deep water and alerted a farmer who dragged their car out of the mud with a tractor.*

1980 — 1989

The start of a long hard winter. This was Aldermaston village on 11th December, 1981.

1980: A heavy hailstorm at Wokingham on 7th October caused £8,000 worth of damage to Heathlands Farm, Wokingham.

1981: On the day that caused the ill-fated British Rail High Speed Train to freeze solid, 41,000 homes were without electricity in the county due to ice and snow on 22nd December. Temperatures fell as low as 5F (-15C) in Wokingham. Snow and ice prevailed for most of the month after the 8th, and a lecture in Abingdon by Sir John Mason, Director-General of the Meteorological Office, entitled, "Man's Attempt to Modify the Weather", was postponed until 6th January because of the severe weather! A fierce April blizzard left 300 people stranded on the M4 and winds piled up drifts eight feet deep in the north-west of the county.

1982: A numbing minus 1F (-18C), Berkshire's lowest recorded temperature, was registered at Arborfield on 14th January. Three hundred people were marooned in their cars on the Newbury-Oxford by-pass on 8th January during a heavy snowstorm, and Sir John Mason's lecture was abandoned again because of the inclement weather! On 3rd July there was a remarkable ball lightning incident at Woodland St Mary, where a glowing silvery gold sphere flew around a cottage during a thunderstorm. The TV set exploded, a refrigerator buzzed and the bathroom window blew outwards. A lightning strike cut a trench in nearby ground. There were tornadoes on 9th December in Bracknell with five roads blocked by fallen trees.

1983: In what was the warmest month since records were correlated in 1659, a powerful supercell thunderstorm caused extensive damage in the north-east of Wokingham on 23rd July. Easthampstead had 1.7 inches (43mm) of rain. The previous day hailstorms had badly affected Cookham and Bray.

1984: At Didcot a tornado damaged 12 properties in the early morning of 23rd November. Witnesses said it sounded like a jet aircraft passing low over their houses.

1985: A cold January with the mercury rising no higher than 24F (-4C) on the 16th at Bracknell. Snow on 9th February piled up in the near gale force winds producing cornice drifts in the lanes of West Berkshire, and major roads were blocked crossing the Berkshire Downs. On 25th June a tornado once again hit Didcot. A large summerhouse was blown over a 10 feet high bush. A lovely September, dry and warm. On Saturday, 9th November at around 8.50am drivers at junction 14 on the M4 near Wickham suddenly encountered a wall of hail. Visibility was nil. A spate of accidents ensued, one car turning a complete somersault.

1986: The second coldest February of the century after 1947 with an average temperature of 30F (-1C). A severe storm on 5th June produced more than two inches of rain (52.5mm) in an hour and a half and a hundred acres of barley were flattened as hail drifted to a depth of 18 inches. Cycle racers in the area suffered cuts and bruises as they were battered by hail the size of golf balls. At Chaddleworth, one farm sustained £30,000 worth of damage while at Beedon congealed hail floated down flooded streets like "icebergs". A tornado struck Winkfield on 22nd August, and ex-hurricane Charlie led to a washout August Bank Holiday with around 1.2 inches (30mm) of rain. The *Maidenhead Advertiser* called it a "Blank Holiday".

1987: On 12th January the mercury failed to rise above 20F (-7C) in Reading, colder than the notoriously freezing days of 1947 or 1963. Temperatures remained below freezing at Maidenhead from late morning on 10th January to mid afternoon on the 15th and then for another 84 hours from early evening the next day. Winds of 80mph on 3rd April left a trail of havoc in Maidenhead. It was the warmest Good Friday since 1949 with 71F (22C) and the wettest October since 1960. The Great Storm of 15th/16th October produced a recorded wind speed of 78mph at Sandhurst.

1988: The sunniest February of the century in some

Membury Service Station where scores of vehicles had been abandoned in the snow.

Snowbound in April

places. Golf ball-sized hail fell and there was much flooding at Cookham on 8th May. Parts of East Berkshire had the warmest Christmas of the century with temperatures topping 57F (14C) on Christmas Eve.

1989: On 25th February the lowest pressure since Christmas 1821 was recorded. An unexpected snowfall on 5th April gave as much as 4 inches (11mm) at Beaufort and on 24th May, as temperatures soared into the eighties, hailstones an inch across fell at Bracknell. At Tilehurst, near Reading, traffic came to a standstill in a deluge of rain and hail. On 6th July severe storms on the Berkshire Downs sent flood waters pouring onto the A4 turning it into a river. At Aldermaston homes were inundated with four feet of water as two ornamental lakes overflowed.

APRIL showers of a different variety were making the headlines during the spring of 1981. During the weekend of April 25th/26th, 300 motorists were stranded on the M4 and 15,000 homes were without electricity due to the worst April snowfall in living memory.

As drifts four feet deep blocked part of the M4, motorists were forced to spend a freezing Saturday night at the Membury Service Station. In the *Evening Post* one policeman was reported as saying: "We couldn't get them out until 11am on Sunday. They had been there all night with no electricity. There was over four feet of snow. You couldn't even see the motorway crash barriers".

While Newbury and Reading escaped the worst of the weather, surrounding villages were cut off and blacked out by fallen trees. In the Reading area, 6,000 homes lost power supplies and in the Inkpen region 9,000 homes were without electricity. At Coombe Gibbet near Inkpen eight motorists were stranded overnight while

those in Lambourn, Kintbury and Great Shefford were completely isolated. The villages of Woodcote, Streatly, Pangbourne and Bradfield also felt the brunt of the conditions.

The weekend was no fun for electricity engineers who worked non-stop mending broken power cables. At the time, Reading SEB was warning that it might be over a week before permanent repairs could be made. Farmers too were struggling to survive the impact of the snow. There was concern for crops as the blizzard took its toll on spring blossom and gale force winds and the weight of snow devastated trees.

The freak freeze was not without its lighter moments. In some villages near Newbury the lack of power produced an ironic problem — food was thawing in deep freezes. Happily there was a company at hand ready to earn itself some publicity. A firm operating an insurance scheme for freezer owners took care of the problem.

The snow was blown into great drifts. This was the Newbury Road, near Brimpton.

Queen stranded in raging blizzard

December 1981 — January 1982

THIS was a winter in which Jack Frost took a firm grip in early December. Berkshire's lowest temperature of the century was recorded, cars were marooned on the motorway for the second time in less than a year, snow drifts reached heights to rival those of 1963 and the Queen, en route to Windsor, had to seek refuge in a Cotswold inn.

It was during the first week of December, 1981 that snow and ice came to the county. Described by the *Slough and Windsor Express* as the worst December since 1901, the sudden icy spell claimed the lives of a milkman from Windsor who died on his rounds and a resident of Sunningdale who collapsed after clearing snow from his drive.

Drivers were caught in the first snow when it fell thickly during the morning rush hour on Tuesday 8th December. There was a repeat dose on Friday 11th. On each occasion cars slithered into ditches, diesel froze in lorry tanks and garage breakdown services were stretched to the limit. Both the M4 and the M3 were closed and roads in East Berkshire, particularly at Windsor, Ascot and Sunningdale were impassable.

On Sunday 13th December, high winds roared across the county, making driving conditions even worse. Trees and power lines were brought down, many homes were blacked out and drifts reached extraordinary heights. Scores of motorists were stranded in their cars and, at Odiham (in Hampshire) 18 families in cars had to be rescued by airmen from

RAF Odiham. In these conditions the Queen, driving from Princess Anne's home, was caught in snowdrifts in the Cotswolds. The four-wheel drive Range Rover became hopelessly snowbound and while snowploughs tried to cut a path through to the M4, the Queen spent four hours receiving the hospitality of the Cross Hands Hotel at Old Sodbury before resuming her journey to Windsor.

On Monday, schools closed due to lack of heating and burst pipes. Criticism, levelled at Berkshire County Council, that the snow caught them unprepared was hotly denied. The county surveyor said they spread a massive 4,000 tons of salt on roads as soon as the weather worsened and then had 100 men on standby to man the snow ploughs. The chaos, he said, was due to the fact that heavy rain washed the salt away and the snow which followed was blown immediately into great drifts. More than 100 fallen trees had to be removed from main roads and workmen had to cope with abandoned cars, vast traffic congestion and gale-force winds.

The snow lay until after Christmas, cleared over the New Year and then returned with a vengeance. Whipped into drifts again by strong winds, the snow brought roads to a standstill between Friday 8th and Sunday 10th January, 1982. More than 300 people were marooned in their cars on the Newbury-Oxford by-pass and chaos returned to the county. The clear skies which followed sent temperatures plumeting to record lows and Berkshire's lowest reading of the century was recorded at Arborfield on 14th January — a numbing -1F (-18C).

Reading is not a town renowned for its beauty; in fact a few writers have cruelly described it as half-baked, artistically null and architecturally hideous. Even John Betjeman, a great enthusiast of Victorian design, is said to have blenched and asked for a restorative glass on seeing the town hall for the first time. Beauty, however, is in the eye of the beholder and those who beheld St John's Hill, Reading on 23rd December, 1981 saw golden garlands and coloured lanterns topped with a crisp mantle of Christmas snow. It was not a classic white Christmas, however, for no snow fell on Christmas Day but it was the prelude to a winter which saw Berkshire's lowest recorded temperature of the century -1F (-18C) on 14th January, 1982.

The bathroom window holed by the ball lightning.

Ball lightning shock on a summer's afternoon

IT was a peaceful late afternoon in Woodland St Mary on 3rd July, 1982. Many people in the village were riveted to their television sets watching the Wimbledon tennis finals. Suddenly a violent squall struck the village with a lashing hail. A vivid stroke of lightning blasted an oak tree, sending a branch crashing to the ground and a power surge put paid to the tennis in nearby houses as television sets were damaged.

Retired couple, Mr and Mrs Bell, were at home in their thatched cottage. Mr Bell was sitting in an armchair when, to his amazement, a bright sphere appeared and floated in front of him, glowing silvery gold, about six inches across and rotating slowly. It flew round the room, then out through an open door and into the bathroom. There followed a terrific bang. It was then that the television exploded.

Mrs Bell was in the kitchen when she saw the passage of the "ball" into the bathroom. When they had recovered themselves sufficiently they investigated and found a hole in the bathroom window pane about 12 inches by eight as though someone had hurled a cricket ball at it, except that most of the broken glass was on the outside. Curiously, there was no evidence of any burning but above the bathroom an immersion heater was damaged and in the kitchen a refrigerator had blown a fuse. A crack had appeared in the living room window sill where a telephone wire was attached although, ironically, the telephone was still working.

Ball lightning is one of the most complex, least known and controversial of meteorological phenomena with no really clear explanation.

July '83 — the hottest month ever

JULY 1983 was Berkshire's hottest month since records began in 1659 — even surpassing the blistering Augusts of 1911, 1947 and 1959. In fact it was so hot that office staff in non-air conditioned buildings fainted, water rationing was threatened and customers at swimming pools quadrupled.

The heatwave fell neatly into the calendar month and as the days progressed the thermometer rose, reaching the nineties on 16th July when three people working in the kitchens of Slough Town Hall collapsed with heat exhaustion. NALGO officials demanded air conditioning and explained that a temperature reading was not possible because the wall thermometer could only reach 120F.

Elsewhere, shopkeepers ran out of ice creams and had to place chocolate bars in the 'fridge. One Reading confectioner said: "Customers are going crackers and buying several boxes of ice cream at a time. Suppliers are doing their best to keep up with demand but we are likely to run out soon".

At Slough, the Baylis Lido welcomed 10,739 swimmers in the first 10 days of July compared with less than 2,000 during the same period the previous summer.

The heatwave sparked a thunderstorm which produced damaging hailstones at Cookham and Bray on 22nd July. Another storm on the following day caused extensive damage in the north-east of Wokingham.

After a succession of damp, cold and even snowbound Easters, the holiday break of 1984 was warm and sunny. The three office girls above prepare for their weekend by splashing out in the Forbury Gardens Pond at Reading in brilliant sunshine.

TEN GREAT FLOODS IN THE THAMES VALLEY

WHEN the great Mississippi River — swollen out of all proportion by the great rains of July 1928 — flooded the surrounding valleys, more than 500,000 people died and 50,000 were made homeless. It still ranks as the greatest meteorological disaster of the twentieth century.

The difference between the Mississippi and the Thames is one of magnitude. Floods bring great personal misery. The loss of property, the damage to health, the fear of similiar catastrophes in the future and the great desire for the authorities to adopt effectual measures to prevent a recurrence of such disasters dominates the thoughts of those who live by the Thames.

The floods in Lynton and Lynmouth in 1952 and those in East Anglia in January 1953 were almost certainly England's most catastrophic. The people of Berkshire, generously supporting the relief fund in both areas, had a good reason for stretching a helping hand to the east and the west. No Thames Valley flood had ever reached such proportions — but what were the greatest floods in the Thames Valley? This is a run-down of the top ten, including those after 1953.

1: 1894 was reported at the time to be the worst in living memory; no exaggeration for once. The Thames, in many places, rose 15 inches and dwellers throughout the county woke up to find that the river had taken possession of their homes.

2: 1809: Difficult to compare with 1894 but in some places the water level was higher and the bridges at Eton, Wallington and Bisham were carried away.

3: 1947: Although flood levels were lower than in 1894, it is the bench mark for comparison because it is still remembered by many people. In Caversham alone, 1,600 houses were inundated and amphibious dukws were borrowed from the War Office.

4: 1990: A flood similiar in intensity to 1974 but more serious in the Maidenhead, Windsor areas because of a large amount of debris on Boulters Weir which could not be removed.

5: 1928: A great deluge of rain combined with thawing snow brought heartbreak. Thameside towns, villages and hamlets from Windsor to Reading found themselves surrounded by water.

6: 1974: Appreciable flooding, particularly in Maidenhead and Bray which lasted three days. More than 500 properties were affected in this area alone. Many people were completely isolated by flood waters.

7: 1979: Floods throughout Berkshire, exacerbated in the east by the partial blockage of Boulters Weir by a sunken barge. This raised the water levels as far as Cookham.

8: 1915: After many days of incessant rain, the tail water at Caversham Lock on 5th January was 10 feet nine inches — two feet below that of 1894. It was particularly bad at Eton and Windsor.

9: 1852: Difficult to compare with those of later years but the November floods were described at the time as one of the greatest ever known. Destined to take a role in folklore as the "Duke of Wellington's floods".

10: 1774: The Thames, flooded by twelve successive days of rain, swept Henley's bridge to ruin. Possibly, greater even than those of 1809 and 1894 but impossible to be precise.

Opposite are two studies by Bill Pike, a well known meteorologist, of the West Berkshire Downs on 10th February, 1985 with an easterly wind blowing snow into drifts near Woodland St Mary. The lower picture shows the snow drifting through an open gateway, looking east towards Roughley from Woodland St Mary. Many main roads were closed by this snowstorm and there were exceptionally strong winds.

Siberia comes to Berkshire

10th — 20th January, 1987

ON MONDAY 12th January, 1987, Berkshire awoke with a shiver. By courtesy of winds from Siberia, the temperature had failed to rise above 19F(7C) all day and, two days later, most of the county was paralysed by the heaviest snowfall for five years. In some communities, particularly on the Downs, there were no buses, no trains, no milk and no post; here, the conditions were the most chaotic since 1963.

The weathermen at Bracknell were given an early indication that frigid air was heading towards England. A killer cold snap, sweeping across Europe, had sent temperatures plunging to some of the lowest values ever known. In Finland it was -31F (-35C) and in Siberia -76F. Moscow was struggling to keep warm at -61F and in Sweden the army was called in to take food and medicine to thousands of homes. The thermometer in Rome was below freezing. Europe seemed to be in the grip of an ice age and Britain was next on the menu.

On Saturday 10th January, as the wind swung round to the north-east, a huge high pressure system was established over Scandinavia. The cold intensified and as the county's snow-plough brigade roused themselves for battle, rising columns of air, cooling and condensing, produced almost non-stop snow showers.

In these conditions thousands of men with gritters and snow-ploughs swept into action drawing on supplies of thousands of tons of salt. It had little effect. By Wednesday evening, Berkshire was covered with a foot of snow and there was huge drifting everywhere.

On the motorway several lorries broke down between Reading and Hungerford when their diesel fuel froze and the Membury Service station was littered with abandoned vehicles. Buses suffered the same problem and scores of train services to London failed to run. There was high drama when a lorry, believed to be carrying nuclear weapons to the Royal Ordnance Factory at Burghfield, skidded off the icy road between Hungerford and Salisbury. Armed guards cordoned off the area and a crane was brought in to right the vehicle.

As the vehicle continued its journey with utmost caution, there were reports of another drama on the M4 near Newbury. A lorry driver, was attempting to thaw out frozen fuel when his diesel tank caught fire and exploded in his face. Suffering horrific burns, he staggered back to his cab and raised the alarm by using his CB radio. He was taken to hospital in Swindon. At Greenham Common, a policeman had his leg broken when a car skidded into his path as he was attempting to stop three 'peace' women from ambushing a Cruise Missile convoy. By 9 am on Tuesday police reported 60 breakdowns on the M4 alone — 500 since the weekend.

On the Downs the conditions were even worse as the wind had strengthened and whipped the loose, powdery snow into great drifts. Schools closed and Berkshire Age Concern was put on red alert as sub-zero temperatures continued to threaten the lives of old folk.

The excessive cold hampered firemen who were called to a blaze at a disused Reading cinema. The water used by 10 appliances froze as it was directed onto the flames and there was a comical touch when icicles formed on the firemen's helmets and hung in front of their faces. Just a few yards away, the heat was intense.

Slowly the wind abated and by Friday, the men on the snow-ploughs and gritters had a more than even chance of winning the battle. They faced acute danger from the icicles, broken drainpipes and hanging gutters that were a feature of many towns but, by the weekend, the roads were in use, buses were running, schools had re-opened, old people were a little warmer, milkmen and postmen had returned and the great thaw had begun, bringing the usual spate of burst pipes and, in the Thames Valley,

There were 500 breakdowns on the M4 in Berkshire during the first three days of the blizzard. Conditions were chaotic.

Far safer to push the bike along Lower Way, Thatcham on 14th January, 1987 — but beware of the car going sideways!

Icicles in Bracknell on the morning of 13th January, 1987 when the minimum temperature was -10C (14F).

Bracknell gets the blame!

16th October, 1987

IN five years Berkshire had experienced almost every weather event that Mother Nature could summon up. A raging blizzard which produced the lowest temperature ever, blistering heat and the hottest month since records began, torrential rain, storm-force winds, hailstones the size of golf balls, two tornadoes, "icebergs" in a village street, killer winds from Siberia and, of course, widespread floods. Were there any more great dramas in store? The weathermen from the Meteorological Office at Bracknell assured the people of Berkshire they could sleep easy. There would always be an early warning.

In the autumn of 1987, the next big warning came. During the second weekend of October, after days of unprecedented rain, Bracknell said that floods were imminent on low-lying ground and in all river valleys. In the Thames Valley, from Windsor down to Reading, police, firemen and officials of the river authority studied their emergency plan procedures. Water was lapping the streets in many towns and villages. It was the expected scenario; sandbags must be prepared.

At 3 pm on Thursday 15th October, the senior duty officer at the Met Office was preparing the afternoon's synoptic review on which all the day's broadcast weather bulletins are based. Anxious to give an accurate flood warning, he studied the information provided, in the form of abstracted summaries by Bracknell's seven-year-old Cyber 205 computer. It showed something else that was just as worrying — a moderate but deepening depression with a centre of 970 millibars just to the north of Cape Finisterre in Spain. A storm was approaching but the data and lack of weather ships made it difficult to ascertain how fast it would deepen and which way it would go.

The duty officer considered what the forecasters should say. There was no doubt that exceptionally strong winds were coming across France, Belgium, Holland and the Channel but would they affect Britain? There was no certainty. The officer stressed the danger of floods in river valleys, underplayed the risk of winds and distributed the night's forecast to the British media. Among them was the BBC's Michael Fish who told his lunchtime viewers in reply to a worried telephone caller — "the weather will become very breezy in the Channel but there won't be a hurricane". It was a remark that was to take a place in weather folklore and make the name of Michael Fish synonymous with "hurricanes".

Twenty four hours later 15 million trees had been lost, lorries and aircraft overturned and church steeples were on the ground. Cars had been crushed by falling trees, entire roofs and walls sucked from houses and 19 people had died. Electricity supplies had failed and 3,000 miles of telephone wires were trailing along country lanes. In most eastern and southern counties, including Berkshire, the landscape had been rearranged. The wind was undoubtedly the cause of such plunder, but who was to blame — God or Bracknell? The full force of the British media turned on the weathermen at the Meteorological Office and the headlines screamed out from every tabloid newspaper in southern England: "Why weren't we warned?"

On Friday and Saturday morning reporters tried in vain to get the official version from Britain's scapegoat for the disaster. Bracknell's telephone contact with the outside world had been severed and they were unable to give an initial defence. It was to be many months — after five Government reports, an official inquiry and long debates in both Houses — before the Secretary of State for Defence observed, with hindsight, that whoever happened to be on duty on 15th October was going to face what was likely to be the severest test of his career.

Dr Houghton, director general of the Meteorological Office was at pains to defend Mr Fish. "He said there would be no hurricane and there was no hurricane". He explained that hurricanes are a particular kind of tropical storm which cannot occur in British latitudes where the sea is never warm enough to stir them up. The 1987 storm reached speeds in excess of 73 miles an hour and was listed as Force 12, which on the Beaufort scale is Hurricane Force. That was good enough for radio, TV and headline writers. To them and to the British public it was a hurricane!

East Berkshire took the full force of the winds. At Windsor, a chimney stack crashed through the roof of the Harte and Garter Hotel killing a woman in an attic bedroom. Firemen had to tunnel through mountains of rubble to reach the body of Patricia Bellwood, a social services consultant.

She was the only person to die in Berkshire but there were many miraculous escapes. A mobile home at The Willows Riverside Park, Windsor was flattened by a falling tree and 75-year-old Mrs Margaret Hand was completely trapped among branches and debris. She was finally pulled out through a hole in the floor. Mrs Valerie Lewis from Britwell endured a night of terror as six trees crashed onto her home. "I have never been so frightened in my life", she told the *Slough Observer*. "They say your life flashes before you at times like this. Mine didn't. It just seized up." Mrs Lewis found herself a prisoner in her own home before being rescued by firemen who spent three hours cutting a way through. They were backed up by the Rapid Support Vehicle from

The all-weather ski slope at Bracknell — now a victim of the weather!

Reading.

Two police officers were patrolling Ascot in the early hours of the morning when a huge tree crashed in front of them. As they turned round another tree fell trapping them. Hours later, with a "hurricane" for company they, too, were rescued by firemen. There was drama also in Caversham where two families escaped with their lives after trees crashed onto their roofs.

In the forests and gardens the work of two hundred years took a few hours to destroy. At Windsor Great Park, more than 2,000 trees were ripped from the ground and the damage was believed to be in excess of £200,000. It took the restoration team more than two years to clear away the trees and replant. It was the same story at Black Park, Slough which lost 6,000 oaks, beeches and birches and at Langley Park where 600 toppled in the wind. At Taplow, the historic Cliveden estate took a battering. Scaffolding on the west side of the building was pulled down damaging the balustrade and National Trust staff found the twisted metal rods mixed up with the tumbled debris of more than 100 trees.

The hurricane force wind bulldozed its way through Reading, felling more than 300 trees and stretching emergency services to the limit. A Southern Electricity spokesman said there had beeen extensive damage to overhead lines and more than 40,000 customers were without a supply. An extra 220 engineers and linesmen were called in from the Midlands to begin the task of re-connecting miles and miles of overhead cables. By noon on Monday electricity had been restored to all but 2,500 in the Ascot and Maidenhead areas.

Newbury and Hungerford were not as badly affected but there were still more than 6,000 customers without power and there were many trees and

This car at Wokingham takes the full impact — a scene repeated throughout southern England.

telegraph poles lying across village roads. There was one romantic windfall. Farmer Ralph Baylis of Winterbourne Manor Farm heard his girlfriend Mary scream as a tree crashed through the roof. Uninjured, but shaken, they went downstairs and drank tea in the darkness. Ralph then proposed and Mary accepted. It was a night they will never forget.

In North Berkshire the winds were powerful enough to rip the roof off a mobile home at Foxhall Manor Park, Didcot and cause many schools to be closed the following day. Here the pressure had dropped to 960 millibars and wind speeds touched 70 miles an hour.

In Southern England there had been nothing to compare with the cost of this storm in modern times. It was the biggest ever payment for damage caused by the weather and certainly the most catastrophic meteorological event that southern England had ever experienced. Such a violent storm, said the experts, was unlikely to occur again for hundreds of years.

The Harte and Garter Hotel, Windsor, where Patricia Bellwood died when a tree fell onto her attic bedroom.

Kay Taylor of Wychcotes, St Peter's Avenue, Caversham who was terrifyingly woken at 3am by a tree falling on the roof above her bedroom.

By the first week of July the weather is usually settled and is kind to Henley's annual regatta — but, of course, that is not always the case. On 3rd July, 1988, rain poured out of the sky in torrents. The show went on, however, while spectators on the water took cover under umbrellas and tarpaulins.

April 1989 and a happy trio enjoy a boat trip on the Thames at Reading under blue skies and a temperature approaching 63F (17C). Within a few days, a snowstorm was raging, the temperature had plunged to 40F (4C) and people were struggling to make headway through the snow.

This light aircraft was lifted up by the winds and deposited on top of a garden fence near White Waltham Airfield in January 1990.

1990 — 1994

1990: A great gale struck on 25th with winds reaching 86mph at Maidenhead and 87mph at Abingdon. Some residents of Newbury were without electricity for a week. At Sandhurst a gust of 93mph was recorded, compared to 78mph in the 1987 storm. On 26th February a driver was killed on the A34 south of Newbury when a tree blew onto his car. In some parts of the Downs 80 per cent of the tree cover was felled. On 8th December, snowstorms completely cut off Lambourn, Peasemoor and Chaddleworth and the A34 and A4 were blocked. Winds gusted to over 50mph. The year was the second warmest in 300 years, the second sunniest behind 1989 and the second driest in 109 years at Wokingham (the driest being 1921).

1991: Ten people died in a multi-vehicle pile up on the M4 near Woodland St Mary on 13th March. Fog was to blame. On 26th September a thunderstorm struck a school at Compton near Newbury. A new fax machine, donated to the school was left smoking when lightning struck the telephone wires.

1992: The driest winter in parts of Berkshire for at least 110 years. Less than two inches (48mm) of rain fell. It was the warmest May in the east of the county since 1833; nine days exceeded 77F (25C).

Thunderstorms on 24th May were quite severe with marble sized hail at Abingdon and a report of Sahara dust at Maidenhead. The 22nd September was the wettest September day for more than 40 years with rainfall of around 2.4 inches (60mm).

1993: Winds exceeding 75mph buffeted some areas on 13th January. February was among the five driest in 125 years (0.15 inches of rain). At Wokingham there was only 0.2 inches in the 52 days up to 20th March. There was also a remarkably high atmospheric pressure. Since the war only one month had been higher, that of February 1959. There was ground frost in July on three nights at Beaufort Park. September was the most sunless for 40 years.

1994: As an area of low pressure crossed southern England on the 6th January, heavy rain abruptly turned to snow at the height of the rush hour with up to four inches in the Bracknell district in one hour. The large flakes were illuminated by vivid flashes of lightning. In a summer which had a good deal of dry and sunny weather, Wokingham had a severe thunderstorm on the night of 24th June with frequent lightning and wind gusting to gale force. 1.7inches (43mm) of rain fell, of which 1.5inches (41mm) fell in only half an hour.

Mist, rain, fog, frosts, floods and the greatest storm of all

December 1989 — February 1990

THE first week of December, 1989 was quiet with mist and fog and sharp overnight frosts. The barometer was high and set on settled weather. After the momentous October, 1987 storm, when statistics such as a 1-in-250-year occurrence were quoted, the surge of ancraophobia was beginning to die down; the winter of 1989 was behaving perfectly normally.

By the end of February, however, Berkshire's beleagured residents had endured an almost unprecedented stormy spell, with February being the windiest on record. Combined with heavy rain and floods, there was little solace in the fact that January and February combined were milder than at any such time since records of temperature began in 1659.

During January, in the Abingdon area, the temperature averaged 50F (10C), worthy of Marseilles on the Mediterranean coast but it would be remembered for the events on Thursday 25th January.

An intense depression developed explosively as it neared Britain and crossed southern Scotland. To the south, over England, lay an area of storm force winds, cutting a swathe of death and destruction. It produced the largest weather-related death toll in Britain since the East Coast floods of 1953.

The scale of the destruction was almost three times that of 1987. Some 80,000 homes in Berkshire and Oxfordshire were plunged into an old-fashioned way of life, without electricity or telephones. Sixteen schools were damaged, 13 miles of the M4 were blocked and 100 roads obstructed by trees and debris. On the A34 south of Abingdon, no less than 17 lorries were blown over and Wallingford was completely cut off at one stage by fallen trees. One road in the Wantage area was blocked by 45 storm wrecked trees. An official from Thames Valley police said that it was the worst event they had ever experienced.

A flood of casualties poured into Reading's Royal Berkshire Hospital. By the end of the day, 200 had been treated for cuts, bruises and even broken limbs caused by flying debris. One man escaped death by a fraction of a second when part of a tree crashed down into Shinfield Road, near Reading University, in front of his car. He survived but many others elsewhere in southern England were crushed to death.

At Greenham Court Primary School near Newbury, pupils were quietly reading when their peace was shattered by a tremendous gust of wind which tore the top corner of a wall from the ceiling of a temporary classroom. A loud command from their teacher, "Move!" led to all of them leaping from their seats and beating a quick retreat and, as the last one bolted out of the door, the wall collapsed and the room was demolished. Elsewhere, at Christ the King Primary School in Reading, pupils were evacuated as the roof blew off and at Easthampstead Park School, windows were blown out and the roof torn apart. Frightened children dived for cover. Southern Electricity answered 10,000 calls by mid-morning on Friday. Helicopters assessed the damage by air and 325 workers on the ground included some from the East Midlands and others suddenly called out of retirement. Some residents in the Pinchington Lane area of Newbury were still without electricity a week after the storm.

The railway line between Reading and Newbury was blocked when a factory roof landed on the tracks and an aircraft made an unauthorised flight when it took off, minus a pilot, and was blown across White Waltham airfield and over two rows of bungalows before landing in a back garden.

Winds gusted to 85 mph at Maidenhead, the highest winds for at least 50 years. At Sandhurst, Mr Heighes recorded 93 mph at 13.49 GMT, 15 mph greater than in 1987. No wonder Sun Alliance received over 7,000 insurance claims in 36 hours. The storm chaos was good news for one firm based in Pangbourne. They spent the weekend repairing 500 glass panes at Kew Gardens.

Any thoughts that the weather would calm down were soon dashed as a further area of low pressure moved north-east along the Channel and rain suddenly turned to snow as the freezing level at cloud height lowered, due to very heavy precipitation. Snow accumulated to four inches in depth around Didcot and some roads became blocked.

Another storm system moved in from the Atlantic on 6th and 7th February, bringing renewed gales and floods. Two schools were closed due to the rising waters in Cookham and Datchet and exclusive houses in Maidenhead, including the homes of Michael Parkinson and Rolf Harris, became awash. A red flood alert was placed on the Thames between Wallingford and Twickenham and more than 40 high-ranking Thames Valley police officers attending a conference at the Moat House Hotel at Sindlesham were marooned by flood water. Berkshire County Council opened its emergency operation centres again, co-ordinating relief from its "underground bunker". Over 200 houses were swamped in Maidenhead.

One hotel guest cheated death in Reading when her bathroom ceiling caved in as a chimney crashed through the roof. She, however, had just gone to a sister hotel to take a dip because the bathroom had been out of use.

Dire warnings from the Met. Office alerted the south to yet another severe storm which duly swept in from the Atlantic on 26th February. This time people lost their lives as winds peaked at between 70 to 80 mph at the height of the rush hour. A cyclist at Winkfield died when he was blown into the path of a car and a driver was crushed in his van by a falling tree on the A34 south of Newbury. Fifty passengers were shocked but unhurt when their train was derailed by a toppled tree lying on the track outside Ascot. A bus was hurled into the path of a lorry in Reading, causing injury to one person. 80,000 homes were left without electricity and water in the Wargrave area. So, what caused this month of storms when up to five million trees were felled nationwide and hundreds of thousands of homes, offices and schools were damaged at an estimated insurance cost of £2 billion. It was a clash of air streams in the Atlantic. Warmer than average seas to the south-west of Britain and colder than average air currents coming south from Greenland caused suitable conditions for sudden explosive deepening of depressions which were swept towards Britain by upper winds or jet streams which at times reached 200mph. "It must be due to global warming", was the comment from all quarters, except meteorologists who said they needed more data to answer that one. Most agreed that a warming of the oceans could lead to greater extremes of weather.

The storm did bring aircraft in from America over an hour early and the water companies were happier than they had been since the previous dry summer. In fact, the winter was the wettest for 108 years at Wokingham; only the years 1914-1915 had had more rain. "Oh, well at least we will not run short of water during the summer", people muttered, especially those that were still drying their homes close to the subsiding Thames. Nature had other ideas and the weather was soon to make headline news of a different kind!

Elizabeth Lewis, aged two and her four-year-old sister, Lucy enjoy the new lake in Remembrance Road, Newbury.

A brick wall collapsed on top of this car at Richfield Avenue, Reading.

*The fierce winds blew several lorries onto their sides on the M4. This was one of the victims —
blown over on the westbound carriageway, near junction 12.*

Just over the border in Hampshire, the lawn of Highclere Castle was littered with fallen cedars.

The vehicle that "can negotiate all conditions" comes to grief near Newbury.

Suddenly there was a lot more water for the swans. A local resident joins them at Riverside Gardens, Purley, near Reading.

One degree (not quite) under! Sheila Ferguson, former member of the group The Three Degrees returned to her home in Bray to find that the only way to get to her front door was by inflatable dinghy. On the trip she enjoyed a little singin' in the rain.

Windsor Castle surrounded by a massive moat. The only raiders in sight were the rising floods.

The water soon found a way round the sandbags at River House, Maidenhead.

The floods near Maidenhead on 8th February, 1990. This was part of a 60-mile stretch of the Thames for which the National Rivers Authority repeated a red flood alert following more torrential rain and storm force winds.

When tarmac turned to treacle and 'triffids' grew in style

The great drought 1989 — 1992

AFTER the fast and furious weather during the winter of 1989-90, conditions quietened down and dropped out of the headlines. However, slowly and almost imperceptibly, a new scourge was to make its presence felt — drought. Only 0.2 inches (5mm) of rain fell at Sandhurst during March 1990; April had no sunless days at all in parts of the county and May recorded only 0.07 inches of rain at Maidenhead. Overall it was the driest Spring since 1844. By the end of July only three inches (77mm) of rain had fallen in five months and the spectre of 1976 was beginning to stalk the land. Rivers such as The Pang ran dry.

The lack of moisture in the soil meant that more of the sun's energy was engaged in heating up the lower atmosphere. The mercury soared. On July 21st it measured 90F (32C). Parts of Reading lost their water supply when excessive demand interrupted the flow. Thames Water embarked on a huge advertising campaign in order to persuade the public to curb their daily consumption which had yearly increased from a rate of 11 litres a day in 1945 to 150 litres by 1990.

The dwindling flow of the rivers had been noticeable after the winter of 1988-89 when, on the Berkshire Downs, winter recharge of the aquifers was only 50 per cent of the average. Evaporation was high during the following summer as temperatures topped 91F (33C) and 1989 proved the sunniest in Wokingham's records with 1,854 hours. The weather is never straightforward and the wild, wet winter which caused so much damage had at least seemed to have solved the problem. The late winter and spring drought that followed put paid to this idea and set the scene for a sweltering performance in July and August.

There was no escape from the heat, even in Snowdonia, where an 80-year-old Berkshire lady collapsed and died in the boiling sun whilst climbing Mount Snowdon.

As temperatures rose during the latter half of July, the countryside was beginning to wilt and it was a case of "share your bath water with a tree" in Windsor. Appeals went out to the public to save their dish and bath water and give it to the trees in the Castle gardens.

As high pressure became established over Germany, very hot air spread north from the Continent. The "dog days" were here. The Romans believed that the combined influence of Sirius the Dog star and the sun made this the hottest time of the year. Today, we know that it is the gradual warming of the oceans which tend to delay the greatest heat until after Midsummer's Day.

As temperatures edged further into the nineties, roads were closed at Finchampstead after tarmac turned to "treacle". On August 2nd, even Big Ben in London stopped, due to the heat. Holidaymakers were warned to stay away from a lake at Dinton Pastures Country Park because of poisonous blue-green algae produced by the action of prolonged sunshine on naturally occurring chemicals in the water or from farm pollution.

Near Eton College, machine guns, axe blades, rifle butts and helmets were revealed sticking out of the dried-up mud from a shrinking stream. It was a hoard of weapons from a local museum's wartime collection that had been stolen.

Just as the storm and flood insurance claims had dried up after the winter gales, subsidence claims poured in from areas with clay soils as the ground fractured and shrank.

Drought interrupted the opening of the Kennet and Avon Canal and the royal barge, Rose of Hungerford, made an ignominious trip by road to Devizes in Wiltshire.

Due to sheer weight of traffic, massive queues built up on the M4 and it was not only car engines which overheated. In spite of temperatures reaching 130F inside the vehicles, Thames Valley Police implored drivers and passengers to stay put and not wander along the motorway.

In gardens there were reports of triffid-like sunflowers growing out of control in the heat.

Friday August 3rd outshone many a Mediterranean resort and was worthy of the Sahara Desert. Unrelenting sunshine from dawn to dusk sent the temperature to new heights in Berkshire. At Mortimer, the mercury soared to 97.7F(36.5C) and at Cheltenham in Gloucestershire a new British record was established with 99F(37.2C). The inevitable hosepipe ban followed in the Thames Water Authority area, affecting 18 million consumers throughout England and Wales. From March 21st to October 2nd there was only one sunless day in many parts of the county. Following the blaze of heat, the temperature fell back some 18F (10C) by Sunday August 5th but the problem of lack of rain continued.

Reservoirs in the east of Berkshire were surprisingly full during 1990 and 1991. The reason was not obvious. Since the 1960's, water levels in the chalk

Left: Ian Silvey of Reading keeps cool in a bubble-bath industrial skip. Right: Lyndsay Hawkins and Paula Richardson in Wokingham on the 3rd August, the day in 1990 when the temperature hit the upper nineties.

below London actually increased due to the reduced demands of industry and enough water having been abstracted from the Thames. However, the actual shortfall of rain by February, 1992 amounted to 19 inches(485mm). The problem was that the sub-surface water table had fallen to unprecedented levels.

In the west of Berkshire, rivers such as the Winterbourne and Lambourn are fed by springs bubbling from aquifers which, as the village names suggest, are naturally intermittent in their flow. But this was serious; rainfall during the winter of 1991-92 was less than 40 per cent and winter recharge of these subterranean water sources fell to less than 30 per cent of the average.

Upstream on the Lambourn, moorhens, dabchicks and coots had disappeared as the river became a mere trickle, in places no more than a muddy puddle. Residents of Boxford were alarmed that natural habitats were being destroyed as oxygen levels were decreasing in the shallow water and dangerous levels of pollutants were building up. The river ran dry at Weston. Controversial schemes for supplying water to new golf courses caused further anxiety in the Newbury area.

The Junior Environment Minister, Mr Tony Baldry, stood in the faltering river Pang at Frilsham, hardly wetting his wellingtons as he saw for himself the dramatic nature of the drought. At Bucklebury, plimsolls were more appropriate!

There was talk of flooding the Enborne Valley to provide a gigantic reservoir for Thames Water, a scheme first mooted in 1908 and last discussed in the 1976 drought, causing panic in the villages of Ashford Hill, Headley and Newtown.

In 1948, a poem was published against a similar scheme in the Newbury Weekly News:

To the few but happy men, born
In the Valley of the Enborne,
Life seems sweet and not so silly
As in the streets of Piccadilly —
But this life will soon be undone
By the Water Board in London,
Who with haste that looks like panic,
Seek to build a dam titanic—
Water Board, they give us reason,
That each Londoner, in season
More than 50 gallons uses,
Of their water, and refuses
To restrict his garden hoses,
Lest he lose his precious roses.

Eventually, the weather put paid to such debates. "Save our local river valleys" was one message on a bridge overlooking The Pang and the elements did just that. At Hamstead Norreys 4 inches (100mm) of rain fell in July, 1992, 5.5 inches (140mm) in August and, by the end of December, over 27 inches had fallen in six months.

The thirsty little rivers, given the kiss of life, bubbled and gurgled again.

More beautiful than stone ornaments these children adorn the park fountain in Reading during the August 1990 heatwave

The right train arrives at Newbury in February 1991 — accompanied by the wrong type of snow!

British Rail puts its services on ice

February, 1991

THE heaviest snow for more than four years fell on the county during February 1991 and, as the wind chill factor pushed temperatures down to 12F (-11C), chaos enveloped the county.

Driving was treacherous as the overnight snow on 6th February turned to ice. Abandoned cars littered main roads and motorways and a spate of accidents caused long tailbacks. On this cold Wednesday thousands of commuters struggled to get to work as peak rail services became crippled. British Rail blamed the snow. "It was the wrong type", they said, " the sort that gets into the smallest crevices of a train engine, freezes and brings it to a halt".

At Reading station the sub-zero temperatures froze the electronic information boards. The rail bosses were attacked by Reading MP Sir Tony Durrant who told the House of Commons that they were to blame for failing to cope with plummeting temperatures. "It is chaos now because they were in such chaos to begin with. The rolling stock is probably in the wrong place and it's time it was better organised."

As the Thames Valley braced itself for more snow, the freezing weather claimed the life of a frail pensioner, described as a recluse, who had burnt her garage and furniture in a desperate bid to keep warm. Age Concern in Berkshire immediately warned

that more old people could die of hypothermia.

While commuters and the elderly were depressed, youngsters — especially the very young who had never seen snow — revelled in the conditions. Out came the toboggans and into hospital went the victims. On 10th February, 40 people were treated for sledging injuries in the Royal Berkshire Hospital at Reading. So lethal were the conditions that St John's Ambulance actually sent a special first aid crew to Prospect Park to treat the injured. At Christmas Common, actor Jeremy Irons helped emergency teams rescue a tobogganist and in another incident ambulancemen were unable to get their vehicle on to the slope where a man lay badly hurt. They called a police helicopter to help.

In Newbury the weather completely wrecked Andrew Lloyd Webber's wedding celebration plans. The millionaire who had married Madeleine Gurdon in secret had to postpone a church service and reception because of the appalling travelling conditions. The church blessing and champagne reception at Mr Lloyd Webber's country home near Newbury was planned for the following week.

A gentle thaw followed a further cold night on 12th February.

In February 1991, temperatures plunged to their lowest level for years — well illustrated by this frozen fountain in Forbury Gardens, Reading.

Arctic sea smoke was seen above the River Lambourn at Eastbury at 10 am on 29th December 1992 when the smoke rose one to two metres above the water. This phenomena is caused when intensely cold air blows over a stretch of comparatively warm water.

Gale-force winds caused extensive structural damage and many trees toppled over in West Berkshire on 14th January, 1993. This was the chaotic scene in the Oxford Road, Donnington.

Rime and hoar frost on oak and beech trees at Inholmes Park, West Berkshire at 9.35 am on 3rd January, 1993.

The small town of Faringdon in Old Berkshire was choked by a sea of mud on 26th May, 1993.

The Faringdon mudslide

May 1993

A HUGE thunderstorm broke over west and north-west Berkshire early on Wednesday, 26th May. The rain cascaded down Folly Hill, Faringdon with such force that a swirling wall of silty water swept upon the town, flooding homes and leaving a sea of thick cloying mud in its wake. Other towns and villages also suffered as fierce strokes of lightning damaged homes and power supplies failed.

The weather conditions were ripe for severe storms as there was a layer of warm air, originating from the Continent, sandwiched between cold air above and below, with winds changing direction from north-east to south. There was also plenty of moisture. The result of these conflicting air masses was a dramatic dawn, as cells of cumulo-nimbus clouds moved north-westwards.

Torrential rain came down with almost unimaginable force. At Uffington, 5 inches (128 mm) of rain, almost two months' worth, was measured.

A surge of chalky water swept down from the surrounding hills and Uffington was completely cut off as the intensity of the flood waters overwhelmed fields, homes, gardens and streets. The worst hit building was the Craven Guest House where guests were shepherded to the first floor and their cars towed out of the floods by tractor. At Stockholm Farm, cattle had to be rescued as their barn was inundated. Another farmer spoke of a terrifying wall of water approaching, coming through the gates and then swirling through the house. Some cattle in sheds had water up to their necks and had to be moved, with great difficulty, to higher ground.

It was the same story in Faringdon as a wall of mud washed off the surrounding high ground. Roads were severed and cars abandoned. Fire crews answered 250 calls though there were many people who battled on alone, sweeping, baling and mopping up flood waters unaided by the emergency services.

The centre of Faringdon drew most of the media attention as a silt-laden torrent burst from the hills and, checked for an instant by the high wall of houses, swept from its confines in a Niagara-like cascade, churning and foaming through the town. As the waters receded a sea of mud was left, necessitating a massive clean-up operation involving bulldozers, diggers and the capacity of 22 lorries. Residents had to salvage what they could as carpets were ruined, furniture wrecked and businesses left in shambles. From the London Road, drastically hit by the seething yellow mud slide, to the relative heights of Cromwell Road where the Cromwell Centre was awash, stories abounded of desperate attempts to stem the tide. Thousands of gallons of water were baled by hand from The Magpies, the architectural antiques centre in the old passenger station, as the proprietor and willing helpers tried to stem the flow.

A possible cause of the ferocious mud flow was the tree-felling on the slopes of Folly Hill. Trees, which had anchored the sandy soil, had been replaced and, at the time, there was only an immature sweetcorn crop to stabilise the slope.

As if the rain was not enough, lightning caused a real shock for one Faringdon family. Mr and Mrs Wood suddenly saw their house appear to light up. They smelt burning and ran downstairs to find telephone sockets a charred mess. But worse still, every electrical appliance was damaged. As they surveyed the mayhem the storm continued to rage until suddenly the floods began to pour in. The water quickly reached waist height and despite frantic efforts to stem the flow, it poured through the house lifting floor boards and destroying carpets.

Another woman was shocked to find her nine-month old grandson floating around the living room in his push chair. She had been in another room answering the telephone when the water began to swirl beneath her feet. Frantically she rushed next door to find the floating baby chuckling at his unexpected nautical trip.

At about this time a school bus carrying 12 children from Buscot to Faringdon Infant School was forced to an abrupt halt by abandoned cars. Fierce lightning and deafening crashes of earth-trembling thunder terrified the children and the driver had to comfort the youngsters. In the National Trust village of Buscot, 20 of the 22 homes were flooded. It was fortunate that repairs to the spillway of a lake in Buscot Park had been carried out or even greater flooding may have resulted. As it was, a hydrological engineer, called in to inspect the lake, said the intensity of the rainfall was a 1 in 260 year occurrence.

Our weather is full of reversals and the stricken River Lambourn at the height of the drought was a woeful sight. Yet a year later the river in spate burst its banks and came hurtling through the streets of Lambourn, Eastbury, East Garston and Great Shefford. One woman watched helplessly when water filled the downstairs bath! The Lamb pub, newly refurbished, was ruined. Eastbury was cut off and 15 houses flooded. At Great Shefford, a wall of yellow-brown water swept through homes reaching a depth of three feet at the Swan pub.

The water caused a fire which gutted a juggernaut's cab near Hungerford Newtown when the ingress of the torrential rain shorted electrical equipment.

In the days that followed, there was a hum of dehumidifiers from a hundred homes trying to make good the heart-rending damage that flood water exacts. They could do nothing for crumbling kitchen units, warped furniture and burst floor boards.

The people of Faringdon tried to stem the tide but the flow of mud was ferocious. A great clean-up operation involved diggers, bulldozers and 22 lorries but carpets were ruined, furniture wrecked and businesses left in shambles.

The River Lambourn, a woeful sight in the drought a year earlier, now showed all its pent-up fury and burst into the streets of Lambourn. At Eastbury, the village was completely cut off.

Black Wednesday in Windsor

The torrential rain of 12th October, 1993, known in Slough and Windsor as Black Wednesday because dirty floodwater inundated hundreds of homes, was so severe that some people found their cars totally submerged.

In Windsor, 120 people had to be evacuated in the Bolton Road area as floods, five feet deep swept into their homes. Children and old people were rescued by firemen and soldiers from the Household Cavalry Regiment who used dinghies and inflatables.

Richard Munt, who was woken by screams, told the *Slough Observer* that he looked out of his bedroom window and saw dustbins, debris and milk bottles floating past the front door. "There was a river outside the house. It was unbelievable".

Picture above, which was taken as the water receded, shows some of the residents of the Boltons displaying a little bit of wartime spirit. On the right, the scene in Victor Road, Windsor.

The two cars which were trapped in the swirling floodwaters of the River Loddon on 14th January 1994, at Land's End — again.

Terrified drivers were swept down river

THERE was more great drama in Berkshire in January 1994. As an area of low pressure crossed southern England, torrential rain pounded the river valleys, eventually turning to snow. There were flooded roads everywhere and a spate of accidents, but nowhere was the situation more dramatic than at Charvil, near Maidenhead where the infamous Land's End ford claimed more victims.

Paul Bird, aged 21, was driving his Ford Escort towards Hurst when he decided to see if the ford by the Land's End pub was still passable. The market post read 18 inches, so Paul thought he would test the depth by placing the two front wheels of the car in the water. He inched forward and suddenly found himself being swept along the River Loddon by the strong current, which had just taken the wheels away.

The terrified driver couldn't open the door because of the force of the water. The car bounced along and eventually came to an abrupt halt only because it hit another car which had earlier met the same fate. Paul managed to squeeze a window open, climbed out, swam with difficulty to the pub and called for help.

The first couple were a man and his wife who drove into the ford and found themselves sailing down the river at a furious pace. Their car struck a bend, preventing it going any further. They managed to free themselves from their safety belts and scramble up a bank.

Mr Ian Lucken who lives near the River Loddon told the *Maidenhead Advertiser* that drivers don't realise the depth of the ford and strength of the current. "It's only a matter of time before someone is killed", he said.

He recommended that a decent road and a bridge be built.

Motorway fog — the tragedies mount

IT has been dubbed 'motorway madness'. The thing that compels ordinary, reasonable people to drive at excessive speeds, oblivious to their surroundings and with complete disregard for other road users. When conditions are good, most of the time people get away with it, but if the insanity is combined with bad weather, this is when tragedy occurs.

Maybe they were late for work, maybe driving the same journey day in, day out had numbed their common sense. Whatever the reasons, ten people never lived to explain why they joined the mass of mangled wreckage when fog hit the M4 in the early morning of 13th March, 1991.

The accident happened near Woodland St Mary in a shallow cutting on a plateau of the West Berkshire Downs. For those drivers on the motorway, conditions were deteriorating rapidly. By 7 am, when the tragedy occurred, visibility had been reduced to 50 metres.

Suddenly there was a loud, explosive bang and the normal incessant roar of eastbound traffic fell silent, as did the birds. A cloud of dark smoke appeared above the white fog and temporarily obscured the sun. Tragically, the BBC Radio 4 weather forecast, warning of dense fog patches came too late for many people as car upon car piled into one another.

Ten people died in the accident and so fierce was the resulting inferno, the surface of the carriageway melted. By 8.45 am, the fog had all but cleared, the wailing of emergency sirens had ceased and the only thing to disturb an otherwise perfect spring day was the 'chopping' sound of what was to become a melee of police and media helicopters.

The morning of Saturday, 9th November, 1985 was typically grey and drizzly. Drivers heading west on the M4 were observing the speed limit and conditions were normal. Suddenly, without any warning, the light rain turned to heavy hail, the wind picked up speed and drivers were blinded as hailstones the size of peas pounded against their windscreens.

The transformation occurred in the space of just six minutes and the storm itself lasted less than 60 seconds. Chaos reigned as drivers attempted to deal with a situation of zero visibility. A policeman who arrived at the scene 20 minutes later noticed that the hail was still more than an inch deep on the hard shoulder. "They talk about motorway madness", he later said, "but this seems to be like trying to drive on ball bearings".

Can catastrophes like these be avoided? Nothing can eliminate the disorientation that occurs as drivers plunge into dense fog or are blinded by hailstones, but there has to be a case for driving at a speed, and with an awareness, appropriate to the conditions.

SIX GLORIOUS BERKSHIRE SUMMERS

1911 At Finchampstead there were eight days in July and six days in August when the mercury exceeded 90F(32C) reaching 97F(36C) at Wokingham. During the three summer months some 838 hours of sunshine were recorded in the Reading area.

1933 Just 2.26 inches (58mm) of rain fell at Upton during the whole of the summer months June to August. It was very sunny with over 200 hours of sunshine above the average. Temperatures were more like that of the Loire Valley in France. The fine weather continued into September with over six hours of average sunshine a day.

1947 After the severe winter the summer made amends and began early in May with temperatures nudging towards the nineties at the end. August was particularly outstanding with daytime temperatures averaging 81F(27C) and ranks as probably the warmest August on record over England as a whole.

1959 Summer began in May when on 12th the mercury reached 82F(28C) at Finchampstead with 7.5 hours of sun a day at Shinfield. Temperatures exceeded 90F(32C) in July. The fine weather continued through September, the sunniest since 1911 with over 7.5 hours of sunshine a day and 80F was recorded as late as 3rd October. It was also the driest period since 1727.

1976 A summer remarkable for its warmth, in England the warmest three summer months equal with 1826 in a series back to 1659. The spell 23rd June to 8th July was unprecedented, the temperature exceeding 90F(32C) somewhere in southern England on each day during this period.

1990 A summer which brought record heat to Berkshire, 97F(36C) and overall the second warmest in 300 years and the second sunniest of the twentieth century with over 1,850 hours of sun in many places. The previous summer had also been outstanding and it added fuel to the global warming debate.

The world's weather comes from Bracknell

BRACKNELL is synonymous with weather. The well-known forecasters on television, the punctilious shipping forecast on radio and the weather reports in daily newspapers all originate from a high rise building in Bracknell, a key centre in monitoring the world's weather.

From the outside there is little evidence to the untrained eye that the weather is being monitored. No Stevenson screen, the weatherman's white louvred box storing instruments, no rain gauge or anemometer. Deep within the building, though, lie some of the world's most powerful computers and weather information is fed into them from all over the world. Reports from 2,500 ships a day, hundreds of aircraft, 2,000 overseas land stations, 100 weather stations in Britain and data from radio sonde balloons, giving upper air information, satellites and radar scanners. All this information is processed in unimaginable amounts, over four calculations for everybody on the planet per second. A trillion equations go to make up a forecast for five days ahead that is as accurate now as a one day forecast ten years ago.

The Meteorological Office has come a long way from its inception in 1854 as a small department within the Board of Trade. In 1860 telegraph speeded the reception of weather reports and the following year storm warnings were first issued. A hay harvest service was started in 1879 and in 1910 outlooks were added to a daily weather forecast. In 1922 the BBC broadcast the first public weather forecast and in 1936 it went out in caption format on television.

In 1944 the most famous forecasts of all, those for the D-Day landings, were brilliantly devised though forecasters largely remained out of public view, that is until 1954 when live weather presentations on the BBC made George Cowling a household name.

It was on a brilliantly sunny morning on 1st November, 1961 that various branches of the Meteorological Office, scattered in Dunstable, Harrow and Kingsway, were brought together in a new building within a new town. By the mid-sixties,

A British Isles forecaster at work in the Met Office, Bracknell on 27th April, 1992.

satellite pictures were being received and computers had been installed. A training centre was established at Shinfield Park, Reading in 1970. Computers continued to become more sophisticated and the new Richardson wing, housing the country's most powerful machine, was added in 1972, named after the first exponent of numerical forecasting in 1916.

The 1980's saw Bracknell become the world area forecast centre for civil aviation; the obstinate magnetic symbols that had a mind of their own on TV weather maps and brought panic "on air" to more than one presenter, disappeared as computer graphics took over. A network of weather radar was established to locate where any rain, sleet, hail or snow was falling nationwide. The latest developments have seen a super computer, Cray C90, perform the work previously carried out by several others at six times the speed.

In the building adjacent to a roundabout that bears the same name, "The Met Office", 1,100 personnel work as a national service for the collection, analysis and supply of weather information.

INDEX

Bob Ogley

BOB was a journalist for 30 years until leaving the editorship of the *Sevenoaks Chronicle* in 1989 to become a full-time publisher and author. The overnight success of his first book *In The Wake of The Hurricane*, which became a national bestseller in both editions, launched him into publishing in the most dramatic way and he has since written a further six books. In 1990 he wrote *Biggin on The Bump*, the history of the RAF fighter station at Biggin Hill, which received tremendous reviews from national, local and aviation press. The book raised £15,000 in author's royalties for the RAF Benevolent Fund. His latest effort is *Doodlebugs and Rockets - the Story of the Flying Bombs*.

Bob has raised a further £60,000 with the hurricane books for environmental charities and has discovered a supplementary career as a speaker to clubs and organisations. Recently he has teamed up with Ian Currie and Mark Davison to research, write and publish the history of the weather in Kent, Sussex, Essex, Norfolk and Suffolk, Hampshire and the Isle of Wight. *The Berkshire Weather Book* is the seventh of a new county weather series.

Ian Currie

THE ever-changing moods and patterns in our weather have always fascinated Ian Currie. He has vivid childhood memories of the 1958 thunderstorm and the deep winter snows of 1962-63, living then near Chislehurst in Kent. Sharing his interest with others has always been a feature of Ian's life. He writes a weekly weather column for several newspapers as well as being a weatherman for Radio Mercury and County Sound.

A graduate of Geography and Earth Science and teacher for 20 years, Ian is now a full-time writer and speaker to clubs and societies all over South-East England. He is a Fellow of the Royal Meteorological Society and a member of the Climatological Observers Link. Together with Mark Davison he has written *Surrey in The Hurricane, London's Hurricane* and *The Surrey Weather Book*. and *Red Sky at Night -Weather Sayings For All Seasons*.

Mark Davison

MARK has been in local journalism for 15 years and is currently deputy editor of the *Surrey Mirror Series*. He is co-author of six county books on weather events and has shown a keen interest in the climate since the big freeze of 1962-3 when, as a small child, he was spell-bound by the heavy falls of snow. In January 1987 his interest was totally renewed.

Risking whatever the elements might try and throw at him, he has ventured out on many wild nights to gather first-hand accounts of the South East's storms and freezes. Together with Ian Currie he has produced a set of postcards commemorating the severe cold spell in February, 1991.

Froglets' Books

In The Wake of The Hurricane
(National Edition Hardback)
ISBN 0 9513019 4 2......................................£9.95

Surrey in The Hurricane
ISBN 0 9513019 2 6....................................£7.50

London's Hurricane
(Paperback) ISBN 0 9513019 3 4.................£4.95
(Hardback) ISBN 0 9513019 8 5.................£7.95

Eye on The Hurricane
(Eastern Counties)
(Paperback) ISBN 0 9513019 6 9.................£7.95
(Hardback) ISBN 0 9513019 7 7...............£11.95

Biggin On The Bump (The most
famous fighter station in the world).
ISBN 1 872337 10 4....................................£9.50

The Surrey Weather Book
Published by Frosted Earth
ISBN 0 9516710 1 4....................................£7.50

The Sussex Weather Book
ISBN 1 872337 30 9....................................£9.95

The Kent Weather Book
ISBN 1 872337 35 X................................£9.95

The Norfolk and Suffolk Weather Book
Paperback ISBN 1 872337 99 6....................£9.95
Hardback ISBN 1 872337 98 8...................£16.95

The Essex Weather Book
ISBN 1 872337 66 X................................£9.95

The Hampshire and Isle of Wight Weather Book
ISBN 1 872337 20 1....................................£9.95

Doodlebugs and Rockets (The Battle
of the Flying Bombs)
(Hardback) ISBN 1 872337 22 8...............£16.95
(Paperback) ISBN 1 872337 21 X...............£9.95

Red Sky at Night
Published by Frosted Earth
ISBN 9516710 2 2.....................................£4.95

Flying Bombs over England
(Paperback) ISBN 1 872337 21 X..............£10.99
(Hardback) ISBN 1 872337 22 8................£16.95

If you wish to order any of the books listed on this page please contact Froglets Publications, Brasted Chart, Westerham, Kent TN16 ILY — 0959 562972

Forthcoming titles in our weather series include The Cornwall, Devon, Dorset, Hertfordshire and Cambridge Weather Books.